# Sustainability

## CIBSE Guide L

**CIBSE**
Engineering a sustainable
built environment

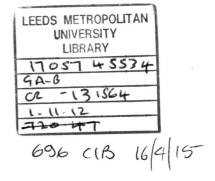

## Note from the publisher

This publication is primarily intended to provide guidance to those responsible for the design, installation, commissioning, operation and maintenance of building services. It is not intended to be exhaustive or definitive and it will be necessary for users of the guidance given to exercise their own professional judgement when deciding whether to abide by or depart from it.

*Printed on 100% recycled paper comprising at least 80% post-consumer waste*

# Foreword

'Sustainability' is very much the flavour of the month. The media are running major articles on the subject on a daily basis and all the political parties are claiming they are greener than their competitors. It is now an issue which will permanently affect and influence all of us. It is here to stay unless we cynically compromise the quality of life of future generations — some would say even the *possibility* of future generations.

Sustainability has always been a major component in the CIBSE portfolio. As an Institution concerned with designing systems which consume less energy and discharge a minimum of harmful contaminants it has long been at the forefront of the sustainability drive. The significance of the CIBSE attitude was driven home at a recent conference when one of the guest speakers suggested that the more appropriate translation of the acronym CIBSE would be the 'Chartered Institution of Building Sustainability Engineers'.

This Guide provides good practice procedures for professionals in the construction industry. It covers disciplines not normally the direct responsibility of the building services engineer, albeit in lesser detail than those that are, because sustainability is the concern of everyone involved in the design, construction, operation and, eventually, the demolition of buildings. Sustainability requires a holistic approach and this is in accord with the acknowledged need for the design team to be multi-disciplinary.

This is the first CIBSE Guide to be accompanied by a searchable online database of good practice measures. This feature will offer major advantages to users and it is planned that future CIBSE Guides will include a similar tool.

The CIBSE Steering Committee and authors were a hardworking and enthusiastic team. I hope architects, engineers, planners, surveyors, developers and all those concerned with buildings will find the output of their endeavours instructive and useful.

Brian Moss
*Chairman, CIBSE Guide L Steering Committee*

## Principal authors

David Cheshire (Faber Maunsell)
Zac Grant (Faber Maunsell)


## Contributing authors

Georgia Arnott (Faber Maunsell)
Miles Attenborough (Faber Maunsell)
Emma Hickling (Faber Maunsell)
Electra Stratigaki (Faber Maunsell)


## Guide L Steering Committee

Brian Moss (Chairman)
Laurence Aston (AMEC)
Andrea Beddard (Arup)
Vic Crisp (CIBSE)
Hywel Davies (CIBSE)
Andrew Ford (Fulcrum Consulting)

## Acknowledgements

Nick Barnard (Faber Maunsell), Chloe Bennett (Faber Maunsell), Ron Decaux, Ruth Fletcher (Faber Maunsell), Aleksandra Krstanovic (Faber Maunsell), Brian Mark (Fulcrum Consulting), Simon Middleditch (Faber Maunsell), Tessa Parnell (Fulcrum Consulting), Ben Smith (Faber Maunsell), Steve Vaughan (Faber Maunsell), Terry Wyatt (Hoare Lea).

This work was part-funded by the CIBSE Research Fund. CIBSE acknowledges the additional support and contribution of Faber Maunsell in the production of this Guide.

**Editor**

Ken Butcher

**CIBSE Research Manager**

Hywel Davies

**CIBSE Publishing Manager**

Jacqueline Balian

# Contents

# Sustainability

## 1 Introduction

This section outlines the scope, purpose and structure of the Guide and associated CIBSE guidance on sustainability.

### 1.1 Purpose of this Guide

This Guide provides building services engineers with guidance on how to respond to the sustainability agenda. It describes:

— the actions that building services engineers should take to enable their work to deliver sustainable outcomes

— how they can influence the work done and decisions made by clients and other professionals.

### 1.2 Scope

Engineers have a huge influence over the energy use, carbon dioxide emissions, water use, thermal comfort, and other sustainability outcomes of buildings. There is increasing pressure to address sustainability issues and to understand how engineering decisions can deliver a more sustainable built environment. For more information on the role of the building services engineer and the sustainability agenda, see the CIBSE's *Introduction to sustainability*[1].

The sustainability agenda as it applies to the built environment is broad and there is no perfect or universally accepted set of headings for organising the issues it covers. This Guide adopts the following headline sustainability issues:

— energy and $CO_2$ emissions

— water use

— adapting buildings for climate change

— flood risk

— sustainable drainage systems

— transport

— ecology and biodiversity

— pollution

— health and wellbeing

— waste

— lifecycle impacts of materials and equipment

— local environment and community.

This set of issues balances a concern for comprehensiveness and clarity with the need to use familiar terms and to focus on issues where engineers have greatest control and influence.

The guidance sets out good and best practice measures beyond what is required to comply with legislation. This Guide is not intended to address legislative requirements.

Whilst many of the examples given in this document to support that behaviour relate to the UK, and there are references to UK legislation, the principles of sustainability apply wherever in the world we practice, and wherever our designs or projects are undertaken.

### 1.3 Intended readership

This Guide is intended for all building services engineers. The sustainable design principles introduced in section 1.7 can and should be applied to all projects. Later sections include examples of specific technologies and techniques that can make projects more sustainable.

### 1.4 Structure

This Guide sets out some fundamental principles which, when followed, will deliver more sustainable buildings. It emphasises the importance of influencing the brief and adopting a strategic approach. It looks at opportunities that are open at the early design stages of a project and includes summaries and case studies of sustainable engineering techniques and technologies.

The CIBSE online sustainable engineering tool[2] (http://www.cibse.org/sustain) is a searchable, online database of good practice guidance. It allows users to generate a shortlist of measures related to a specific sustainability issue, along with references to relevant guidance documents.

The CIBSE's *Introduction to sustainability* explains the origins and meaning of sustainability and the drivers for engineers to contribute to a more sustainable built environment.

Figure 1 below shows how the three elements of the CIBSE's guidance on sustainability relate and the parts of the building lifecycle they address.

### 1.5 The role of engineers in sustainability

Engineers have direct influence over what many would rank as top priority sustainability issues. As such it is

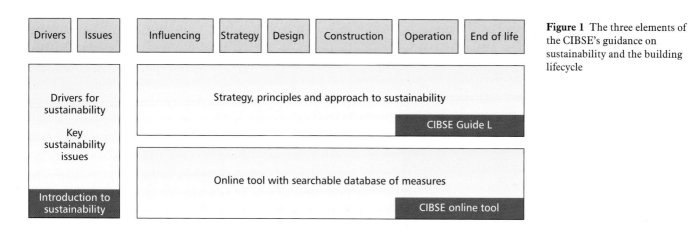

**Figure 1** The three elements of the CIBSE's guidance on sustainability and the building lifecycle

essential for engineers to be involved at the early stages of projects when there is still the maximum scope to integrate appropriate solutions at the lowest possible cost. This may involve challenging the client's brief and contributing to early project and design strategy, ensuring that sustainability issues have been addressed in a comprehensive and coherent way. For example, the engineers should contribute towards decisions about site layout, building form, orientation and building fabric because of the impact these issues have on the sustainability of the whole project.

Service engineers are most likely to have direct control or influence over:

— energy use

— water use

— adapting to climate change

— health and wellbeing (as influenced by thermal comfort, lighting, noise and indoor air quality)

— pollutants from building services

— waste and recycling strategies.

As key members of the project team, building services engineers are also in a position to raise other sustainability issues and contribute to addressing them. This Guide includes an introduction to a number of these issues, including materials selection, sustainable drainage, biodiversity and transport.

## 1.6        How to use Guide L

This Guide is divided into sections broadly corresponding to the lifecycle stages of a building, as follows:

— Section 2: influencing clients and project

— Section 3: sustainability strategy

— Section 4: supporting the planning application

— Section 5: new design and refurbishment

— Section 6: construction

— Section 7: buildings in use

— Section 8: end of life.

Section 2 on 'influencing' and section 3 on 'strategy' are intended as useful background for all projects, from major new development projects through to pre-acquisition surveys for existing buildings.

Section 4 on 'planning', section 5 on 'design' and section 6 on 'construction' will generally be of relevance to both new buildings and major refurbishments. Section 7 on 'operation' covers facilities and energy management, maintenance, minor works etc. and section 8 on 'end of life' considers decommissioning and demolition of a building.

## 1.7        Principles of sustainability

A set of principles are used to underpin the key sections of the document. These principles can be applied, as appropriate, on projects. These principles are applied to each of the sustainability issues as shown in Table 1.

These principles are used as the structure for the guidance in this Guide and are used to structure the measures in the CIBSE online sustainable engineering tool[2].

## 1.8        Extent of guidance provided

The following sections of this Guide provide guidance on each of the key sustainability issues. Issues fall into two broad categories with corresponding coverage:

— where services engineers have direct control or strong influence (e.g. energy and $CO_2$ emissions) the issue is addressed in some detail and covers the principles, see Figure 2

— where services engineers do not have direct responsibility, the Guide concentrates on early strategy and aims to provide enough background and information to allow engineers to understand the issues at stake and contribute project ideas, see Figure 3.

# 2        Influencing clients and projects

This section sets out how building services engineers can make projects more sustainable by giving advice at the start of a project and by influencing the project brief.

## 2.1        Influencing the strategic brief

It is good practice for clients to prepare a strategic brief for a new development or other major project. One purpose of

**Table 1** Principles of sustainability

| Issue | Principles to be applied |
|---|---|
| Energy and $CO_2$ emissions | Reduce demand<br>Meet end use demand efficiently<br>Supply from low carbon sources<br>Supply from renewable sources<br>Enable energy management |
| Water use | Reduce demand (and waste)<br>Meet demand efficiently<br>Supply collected rainwater or recycled grey water<br>Recycle black water close to the point of use, if appropriate<br>Enable water management |
| Adapting buildings for climate change | Reduce unnecessary heat gains<br>Make effective use of thermal mass<br>Apply an appropriate ventilation strategy<br>Apply active cooling<br>Enable future adaptability |
| Flood risk | Avoid locations at higher risk of flooding<br>Reduce the risk of flooding<br>Avoid increasing off site flood risks<br>Design for flood resilience where necessary |
| Sustainable drainage systems | Reduce run-off from the site<br>Attenuate run-off from the site<br>Use or enhance natural drainage systems and/or techniques modelled on them<br>Provide additional benefits (amenity, habitats, etc.) |
| Transport | Reduce use of private cars<br>Enable walking and cycling<br>Enable use of public transport<br>Enable provision of information on sustainable modes of transport |
| Ecology and biodiversity | Conserve, protect, and enhance site ecology<br>Provide new and enhanced habitats<br>Increase the number of appropriate species and their populations<br>Compensate for any unavoidable ecological damage or loss of biodiversity |
| Pollution | Prevent or reduce pollution at source<br>Treat unpreventable pollution in an environmentally safe manner<br>Undertake disposal of pollutants as a last resort and in an environmentally safe manner |
| Health and wellbeing | Discharge all statutory health and safety obligations<br>Apply good practice in providing for the widest practical range of accessibility needs<br>Avoid or reduce health risk factors<br>Provide comfortable internal conditions |
| Waste | Reduce waste<br>Reuse materials and equipment (and facilitate future re-use)<br>Recycle waste (and facilitate recycling)<br>Compost biodegradable waste<br>Recover energy from waste (and facilitate energy recovery from waste) |
| Lifecycle impacts of materials and equipment | Select materials and equipment from sustainable sources<br>Select materials and equipment with the lowest in-use environmental impacts<br>Select materials and equipment with the lowest embodied environmental impacts<br>Select materials and equipment with high recycled content |
| Local environment and community | Engage with the local community throughout the building lifecycle<br>Maintain and enhance environmental quality<br>Avoid nuisance pollution levels (including noise)<br>Avoid causing other nuisances to neighbourhood building users |

such a brief is to provide consultants with a solid basis on which to tender for consultancy services. Sustainability objectives, targets, and criteria for measuring performance and determining success should form an integral part of the briefing process from the inception of a project.

If a strategic brief does not cover sustainability, then services engineers should consider the drivers for addressing sustainability issues early in a project. The CIBSE's *Introduction to sustainability*[1] identifies some of the key drivers for projects, such as legislation (building regulations), planning policies and client requirements. Raising issues early may uncover the existence of unexpected requirements arising from, for example, regional and local planning policies, building regulations, and the client's own corporate social responsibility policies, etc. Integrating sustainable solutions from the start may save considerable time, effort and money later on. The opportunity to raise sustainability issues at this stage in the project should not be missed.

Water use principles:
— reduce demand (and waste)
— meet demand efficiently
— supply collected rainwater or recycled grey water
— recycle black water close to the point of use, if appropriate
— enable water management

| Strategy | Design |
|---|---|
| **Water management strategy** | **Water efficiency design** |
| Principles: | Principles: |
| — infrastructure capacity<br>— predict demand and discharge rates<br>— reduce water demand<br>— water efficiency<br>— distribution and supply modes<br>— key actions | — review infrastructure capacity<br>— predict demand for the building<br>— reduce demand<br>— water efficiency<br>— recycled/reclaimed water<br>— key actions |

**Figure 2** Strategy and design guidance where services engineers have direct control

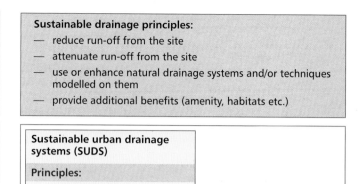

Sustainable drainage principles:
— reduce run-off from the site
— attenuate run-off from the site
— use or enhance natural drainage systems and/or techniques modelled on them
— provide additional benefits (amenity, habitats etc.)

Sustainable urban drainage systems (SUDS)
Principles:
— example measures
— integrating SUDS and rainwater collection
— SUDS and living roofs
— key actions

Issues that are directly relevant to building services engineers

**Figure 3** Strategy and design guidance where services engineers have indirect influence

## 2.2 Agreeing realistic and measurable targets

Wherever possible, sustainability objectives in the project brief should be clarified and reinforced with performance standards. Table 2 shows examples of sustainability objectives that could be included in a strategic brief along with corresponding indicators and performance standards for the set of headline sustainability issues. Some issues, e.g. flood risk, will primarily be the responsibility of other project team members, but almost all have some relationship with building services.

There are many sources of performance standards for sustainability issues in buildings. In particular, BREEAM[3] and the *Code for Sustainable Homes*[4] (previously EcoHomes) in the UK, include good practice criteria for a range of environmental issues. NABERS[7] in Australia and HK-BEAM[8] in Hong Kong include good practice criteria for a range of environmental issues.

Information on incorporating sustainability into the brief is set out in CIRIA publication C571[9] and OGC Procurement Guide 11: *Sustainability*[10].

## 2.3 Understanding client needs

Building services engineers must have an in-depth understanding of a client's needs if they are to provide appropriate technical solutions. It is recommended that the project team works to obtain a concise, non-technical statement of the functions required to be performed by the building services. BSRIA AG1/90: *A design briefing manual*[11] provides a useful decision tool for providing such a statement.

The project team should reconfirm the brief with the client by preparing a 'reflected brief'. Firming-up the brief at an early stage is essential for a successful project. For more information see Construction Industry Board Report: *Briefing the team*[12].

Building services engineers should review the performance standards proposed in the brief and ensure that they do not contradict the sustainability aspirations for the project. For example, the environmental design criteria may include thermal comfort requirements that can only be achieved by using energy-intensive engineering solutions.

## 2.4 Terms of appointment

Building services engineers have an opportunity to expand their roles and provide sustainability advice on projects. Therefore, it is important that they consider sustainability before being appointed and that sustainability advice is offered, even if this is not included in the brief.

As a minimum, a review of planning policies should be undertaken before being appointed and engineers should establish whether support for the planning application is included in the scope of work. As planning is becoming a key driver for sustainability, project teams are increasingly reliant on engineers to provide advice on carbon emissions, water use, microclimate, internal conditions etc. More information on planning is provided in section 4.

In particular, when engineers are appointed as the lead consultant (e.g. under item A2 of the Association for Consultancy and Engineering (ACE) conditions), then they are in a strong position to be able to take a lead in sustainability.

The RIBA *Architect's Plan of Work*[13] states that services engineers should 'advise on sustainable development' at Stage C. However, it is increasingly important for building services engineers to be involved as early as possible in projects as they will be required to provide advice on key issues such as site layout, built form and the building envelope.

Currently, the ACE conditions do not make reference to sustainability or to the work associated with planning applications. Therefore, it is very important that building

**Table 2** Example of sustainability objectives (and related indicators and performance standards) for a strategic brief

| Issue | Typical design and construction objective | Example indicators | Example performance standards |
|---|---|---|---|
| Energy and $CO_2$ | Reduce predicted $CO_2$ emissions by applying energy efficient design principles and utilising low or zero carbon technologies | Total $CO_2$ emissions: $(kgCO_2/m^2)/year$ Air permeability index: $(m^3/h)/m^2$ at 50 Pa | Non-domestic: 50 $kgCO_2/m^2$ (all uses) Dwellings: DER* of 18 $kgCO_2/m^2$; Air permeability: 5 $(m^3/h)/m^2$ at 50 Pa |
| Water | Reduce predicted water use by integrating water efficient plant, appliances and fittings | Non-domestic: $(m^3/person)/year$ or (litre/person)/day Dwellings: $(m^3/bedspace)/year$ or (litre/person)/day | Non-domestic: 1.5 $(m^3/person)/year$ Dwellings: 105 (litre/person)/day |
| Waste | Reduce construction and demolition waste to landfill and enable in use recycling by following the waste hierarchy | Tonnes waste; % recycled | Achieve BREEAM[3]/*Code for Sustainable Homes*[4] waste credits |
| Transport | Increase the use of sustainable modes of transport when the building is in use | Percentage of trips by each mode of transport (%) | Achieve BREEAM[3] transport credits |
| Adapting to climate change | Improve the capacity of the building to operate successfully under the different and demanding conditions predicted in future | Predicted hours of summertime overheating | Predicted temperatures not to exceed 25 °C for more than 5% of the year and/or exceed 28 °C for more than 1% of the year |
| Flood risk | Mitigate the risk of flooding (and design for flood resilience) | — | Flood Risk Assessment (FRA): achieve BREEAM[3]/*Code for Sustainable Homes*[4] flood risk credits |
| Materials | Reduce the embodied lifetime environmental impacts by selecting on the basis of environmental preference, e.g. recycled content | Percentage achieving preference criteria (%) | *Green Guides*[5,6] 'A-rated' constructions; 10% of materials by value have high recycled content |
| Pollution | Reduce unavoidable building related emissions and the risk of accidental pollution | Global warming potential (GWP); $mgNO_x/kW{\cdot}h$ delivered energy | Achieve BREEAM[3]/*Code for Sustainable Homes*[4] pollution credits; zero GWP/ODP refrigerants and insulants |
| Ecology and biodiversity | Enhance the ecology and biodiversity of the site by protecting existing assets and by introducing new habitats and/or species | Change in site species density | Achieve BREEAM[3]/*Code for Sustainable Homes*[4] ecology credits; address local biodiversity action plan (LBAP) |
| Health and wellbeing | Provide a safer, more accessible, healthy and comfortable environment | — | Achieve Lifetime Homes accessibility standard; low VOC finishes |
| Social issues | Reduce crime and adverse effects on neighbours throughout the lifetime of the development through design and good practice in construction and operation | — | Achieve Secured by Design 'Developer's Award' |

* DER: dwelling $CO_2$ emission rate (Building Regulations)

*Note*: this table is for illustrative purposes only; it will be part of the project team's role to identify an appropriate set of objectives and targets for the specific project.

services engineers determine what work may be generated by sustainability requirements and the contribution to the planning application. This work can then be explicitly included (or excluded) from the scope and fees. Engineers are likely to be expected to provide advice on:

— reducing carbon emissions, including influencing the built form and building envelope

— reducing water use

— adapting buildings to climate change, requiring early assessment of internal conditions and vulnerability to flooding

— health and wellbeing (as influenced by thermal comfort, lighting, noise and indoor air quality)

— environmental impacts from building services that would have to be addressed in an environmental impact assessment, and

— waste and recycling strategies for proposals.

Due to the changes in the planning system and the increased emphasis on carbon emissions and water use, it is likely that advice on reducing both carbon emissions and water use will be required very early in a project. Therefore, it is important to ensure that the scope of work includes an adequate amount of time to address these issues in the work leading up to the submission of a planning application.

Engineers could also offer advice on the other sustainability issues addressed within this Guide.

Some sustainable technologies may require innovative approaches that are not well proven on a wide scale. One of the roles of building services engineers will be to identify and explain these risks to the client.

Figure 4 summarises the relationship between the RIBA's *Architect's Plan of Work*[13], the 2002 ACE work stages and the sections of this Guide.

| CIBSE Guide L section | RIBA Architect's Plan of Work | | ACE 2002 Work Stage |
|---|---|---|---|
| | Work Stage | Title | |
| Section 2: Influencing clients and projects | Pre-stage A | Establishing need | |
| Section 3: Sustainability strategy | A | Appraisal | C1 |
| | B | Strategic briefing | C2 |
| Section 4: Supporting the planning application / Section 5: New design and refurbishment | C | Outline proposals | C3 |
| | D | Detailed proposals | C4 |
| | E | Final proposals | C5 |
| | F | Production information | C6 |
| Section 6: Construction | G | Tender documentation | C7 |
| | H | Tender action | |
| | J | Mobilisation | |
| | L | Construction to practical completion | C8 |
| | L | After practical completion | |
| Section 7: Buildings in use | | | |
| Section 8: End of life | | | |

**Figure 4** Relationship of CIBSE Guide L to RIBA *Architect's Plan of Work*[13] and 2002 ACE work stages

## 2.5 Key actions

The key actions for building services engineers prior to appointment are as follows:

— Identify all drivers for sustainability and ensure that the terms of appointment allow for project team to respond to these drivers.

— Identify the necessary tasks to ensure Building Regulations Part L compliance.

— Identify risks associated with project that relate to sustainability (e.g. flood risk assessments, damage to ecological habitat, transport impacts etc.).

— Determine potential impact of sustainability targets (e.g. a target for a 'zero carbon development' is likely to have implications on whole project team).

— Review the performance standards in the brief to identify any conflicts with sustainability aspirations and prepare a response to the brief.

— Include scope and fees for early-stage predictions of energy and water use (early-stage energy/carbon assessments are becoming essential).

— Determine whether an environmental impact assessment is required.

## 3 Sustainability strategy

This section sets out how engineers can inform decisions at the first stages of a project that will have an impact on the built form and layout of the site.

This section broadly relates to RIBA Plan of Work stages A and B.

Section 5 provides guidance related to the design and refurbishment of buildings at RIBA Plan of Work Stages C and D.

The decisions made at the early stages in a project are crucial to ensuring a sustainable outcome for a project.

Strategies for energy, water management and waste are considered separately below. There is also the opportunity to integrate these strategies using techniques such as energy from waste and sewage sludge etc. These technologies and techniques are discussed within each section.

The sustainability strategy is being increasingly influenced by planning policy. See section 4 for more information.

The initial review of the opportunities and constraints of the site should be undertaken from an engineering perspective. This would cover issues such as:

— sources of noise or air pollution

— prevailing wind and wind resource

— sun path and shading from other buildings

— potential biomass resource

— ground conditions for ground source heat pumps heating/cooling

— the constraints of existing buildings.

A review of the existing infrastructure capacity will help to inform the energy, water and drainage strategies and should be undertaken as early as possible.

Building services engineer should provide advice to the project team on key issues that inform the site layout, building form, orientation and building fabric.

## 3.1 Energy and low carbon strategy

The main objective of the energy strategy should be to reduce the $CO_2$ emissions from the proposed development by following the principles set out below. The energy strategy should also aim to reduce the use of finite, non-renewable resources (fossil fuels) and to reduce the other emissions related to building energy use (e.g. $NO_x$ and $SO_x$).

Targets for 'carbon neutral' or 'net zero carbon' developments have been set for some projects. These targets are often interpreted as a development that generates as much energy on-site as it uses over a year (see section 3.1.7.3). These targets are useful to drive change, but the opportunities to generate on-site energy are dependent on a number of issues, relating primarily to site conditions and location. Therefore, it is more appropriate to consider radical reductions in $CO_2$ emissions, rather than necessarily targeting zero emissions.

Design targets have to ensure that buildings are designed to adapt to future climates, in particular the design considerations to reduce the risk of over heating within the internal environment. Section 3.3.2 provides further guidance and references for adapting to climate change.

As part of a low or zero carbon strategy, the carbon emissions from transport associated with the site should also be considered. There are also transport impacts associated with the use of biomass that should be considered as part of the overall aim to reduce carbon emissions. Guidance on how a sustainable transport strategy can be implemented is covered in section 3.6.

### 3.1.1 Energy strategy reports to support the planning application

Energy strategy reports to support the planning application are currently required for major projects in London that are referable to the Greater London Authority (GLA). Some local planning authorities are adopting the same approach as the GLA and it should be considered good practice to develop an energy statement in support of all major planning applications.

The energy strategy report should demonstrate that the project design team has given thorough consideration to all zero and low $CO_2$ technologies that technically could be employed to meet a proportion of the building's energy demand.

The report should establish the building energy demand and show the energy and related $CO_2$ savings that can be made through energy efficiency measures, efficient supply of energy (such as combined heat and power or 'tri-generation' (i.e. simultaneous production of electricity, heat and cooling)) and incorporation of a variety of renewable energy sources. Finally the report should set out the project team's preferred energy strategy.

This section and section 5.1 both include guidance on the approach to developing an Energy Statement and more information can be found in GLA publications: *Integrating renewable energy into new developments: Toolkit for planners, developers and consultants*[14] and *Sustainable Design and Construction — London Plan Supplementary Planning Guidance*[15]. These publications are available from the Greater London Authority (http://www.london.gov.uk).

### 3.1.2 Principles

The principles for developing an energy strategy are:

— reduce demand

— meet end use demand efficiently

— supply from low carbon sources

— supply from renewable sources

— enable energy management.

Refer to the CIBSE on-line sustainable engineering tool[2] for practical measures and sources of guidance for each of these principles (www.cibse.org/sustain).

These principles would be applied by the building services engineer.

### 3.1.3 Site analysis

The first step is to undertake a review of site opportunities and constraints (e.g. ground conditions, wind resource, solar access, drainage capacity, existing buildings, space on site etc.), see Figure 5.

As part of the site analysis, a review of infrastructure capacity needs to be undertaken.

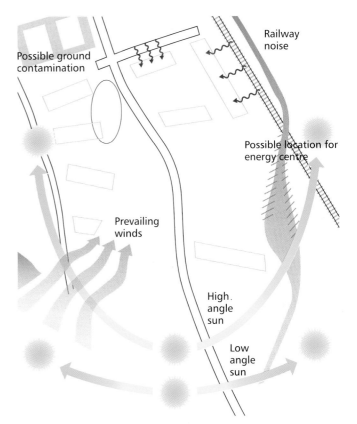

**Figure 5** Energy strategy; site opportunities and constraints

### 3.1.4 Predict site-wide energy demand profiles

The first step in assessing energy supply options is to ascertain the likely total energy demand and demand pattern for any given scheme. From these demands the total site $CO_2$ emissions due to primary energy consumption can be calculated.

For existing buildings, the energy use would be obtained from energy monitoring and utility bill information. For more information on energy management, see section 7.5.

An initial prediction of the energy demand for a proposed development can be made before the design or layout of buildings has been decided. This initial estimate can be made using either benchmark figures or initial modelling using standard building types from previous work. This would give only approximate energy demand figures, but provides a baseline. At this stage in the design process there may not be sufficient detail to create a building model that would be any more accurate than benchmark figures. It is sufficient to understand the approximate loads and the proportion of electricity, heating and cooling required for the site. However, these estimates should only be used to form the initial strategy for the site.

The 'best practice' benchmark figures provided in chapter 5 of CIBSE Guide F: *Energy efficiency in buildings*[16] and the GLA toolkit, *Integrating renewable energy into new developments*[14], are based on monitored data from occupied buildings. These data are now quite old and it is suggested that the benchmarks be adjusted to reflect recent and earlier changes in building regulations and energy efficiency improvements.

While the 2006 edition of Building Regulations Approved Document L2A[17] for England and Wales* requires a 20% to 28% reduction in carbon emissions compared to a notional building, the actual total savings achieved in practice may be lower as the Building Regulations do not cover all end uses of energy. The 2006 Regulations are also based on theoretical design energy use, and real building use may be higher, due to poor operation and management and extended hours of plant operation.

The predicted annual energy demands for gas and electricity should be kept separate and demands for cooling and heating have to be identified separately.

Dynamic thermal modelling should be used to predict energy demands as soon as a built form is proposed. The results of early thermal modelling will help to inform early design decisions and identify any issues that need to be resolved, such as overheating.

It is becoming increasingly important to undertake thermal modelling at the early stages of a project. A prediction of the total carbon emissions from the building will have to be undertaken for any major developments in London and some other local planning authorities (see section 3.1.1 above). This has to be based on a thermal model of the building, rather than on benchmarks.

Further information on how to predict energy demands for individual buildings is set out in section 5.1.

## 3.1.5    Reduce demand

At the site level, there are a number of issues that need to be considered to reduce energy demand and to contribute towards a low/zero carbon strategy. A realistic prediction of the potential energy reduction for the individual buildings should be made, taking into account the proposed energy efficiency measures.

Reducing demand is also about ensuring that the environmental performance criteria in the brief are appropriate and do not, for example, require unnecessarily tight control of internal air temperatures.

More information on reducing demand at the site level can be found in BRE Report 380: *Environmental site layout planning*[18].

### 3.1.5.1    Passive design measures

Passive design uses layout, fabric and form to reduce the cooling, lighting and heating demand.

Passive solar gains can be of benefit for residential buildings in the heating season, but this should be weighed against the risks of overheating in summer and the fact that carbon emissions associated with space heating represent only a small proportion of the total carbon emissions from a dwelling. For commercial buildings with large internal gains, the aim should be to reduce cooling demands from solar gains by reducing excessive glazing and providing appropriate shading.

Passive design is part of the portfolio of measures available for reducing energy demand.

Further information is set out in CIBSE Guide F: *Energy efficiency in buildings*[16] and CIBSE AM10: *Natural ventilation in non-domestic buildings*[19].

### 3.1.5.2    Daylighting

Good daylight design starts at the site layout stage. If neighbouring buildings are large or close by, adequate daylighting can be difficult to achieve. The distribution of light in the room will be affected as well as the total amount received. Further information can be found in BRE Report 380: *Environmental site layout planning*[18].

Frequently occupied areas should be designed to achieve daylighting levels at least in accordance with BS 8206[20]. Daylight levels are calculated from data on glazed area, glass transmission factor, total surface area (walls, floor, ceiling and windows) and typical reflectance properties of internal surfaces.

### 3.1.5.3    Building orientation

Wherever appropriate within the development, buildings should be oriented facing south to allow best exploitation of sunlight while allowing effective control of solar gains in summer. Particular care is required to control solar gain for east/west facing elevations, due to the low summer angles. Appropriate shading is required to limit over-heating in the summer. Roofs should also, wherever practicable, be orientated to be within 45° of south to allow for future incorporation of solar thermal or photo-voltaic panels.

### 3.1.5.4    Shelter and shade

Layouts and landscaping design should be utilised to provide shelter from prevailing winds and natural shading for facades and, wherever possible, to help avoid the potential overheating mentioned above.

### 3.1.5.5    Natural and mechanical ventilation

The ventilation strategy can affect the form and layout of buildings. CIBSE AM10: *Natural ventilation in non-domestic buildings*[19], CIBSE AM13: *Mixed mode ventilation*[21] and BRE Digest 399: *Natural ventilation in non-domestic buildings*[22] provide further information to help identify appropriate ventilation strategies that take into account carbon emissions and internal comfort.

---

* Similar legislation applies in Scotland and Northern Ireland

### 3.1.6 Meet demand efficiently

Once the initial predictions for the energy demand have been reduced as far as possible, assumptions have to be made about the potential reductions that can be made through energy efficient plant and equipment. At early design stages, it would be sufficient to assume a percentage reduction, based on experience and guidance set out in CIBSE Guide F: *Energy efficiency in buildings*[16]. Although the likely contribution from energy efficiency measures will not be known at the early stages in the design, this is an important opportunity to reduce the carbon emissions from the building. Energy efficiency should be addressed in detail as the design is developed.

### 3.1.7 Supply from low and zero carbon (LZC) technologies

Developments are increasingly the subject of specific targets to reduce $CO_2$ emissions. An appraisal of the LZC options should be undertaken early in the design process with predicted $CO_2$ emissions for each LZC option compared against a 'business-as-usual' baseline (e.g. compliant with Building Regulations). $CO_2$ targets for developments are often expressed in terms of the need for:

— low carbon development

— 10% of energy demands met from renewables

— zero carbon development.

#### 3.1.7.1 Low carbon development

There are moves to define this previously generic phrase as meaning a development with carbon emissions 50% lower than the baseline[23]. This form of target provides flexibility in the design solutions available.

#### 3.1.7.2 10% renewables

This form of target constrains the options by requiring the selection of renewable technologies. Despite the typical wording of '10% renewables' policies, the calculations are generally expected to show that the application of renewables achieves a reduction in $CO_2$ emissions of 10% against the baseline.

#### 3.1.7.3 Zero carbon development

This is the most demanding target likely to be applied to new developments. It can be difficult and expensive to achieve. The zero target relates to net emissions over the course of the year. It allows energy use on site giving rise to $CO_2$ emissions as long as this is balanced by the export of energy that abates an equivalent quantity of $CO_2$. It also allows low or zero carbon energy to be imported, subject to rules on 'additionality' (to prevent the target being achieved by simply sequestering the $CO_2$ emissions savings from existing off-site renewable generating capacity)[23].

Biomass heating represents a relatively cost effective option for meeting 100% of heat demand from renewable energy technologies. Achieving 100% renewable electricity supply is more difficult and comes at a higher cost, particularly using building integrated technologies such as building-mounted wind turbines or photovoltaics (PV). Large scale wind turbines and biomass CHP (or tri-generation) are other options, both of which can be very cost effective, if their respective constraints can be overcome. Section 5.1 sets out more information on these technologies.

#### 3.1.7.4 Carbon emission factors

Low and zero carbon developments have to consider the carbon emission factors associated with each source of fuel, particularly the relatively high carbon emissions associated with grid electricity. Carbon emission factors are set out in Figure 6 below.

Grid-displaced electricity is the quantity of site-generated electricity that is exported or used on site (e.g. from photovoltaics, CHP or wind). This reduces the amount of electricity that has to be drawn from the grid. Building Regulations Part L2A for England and Wales specifies a higher carbon emission factor for grid-displaced electricity, meaning that on-site generation reduces a building's carbon emissions.

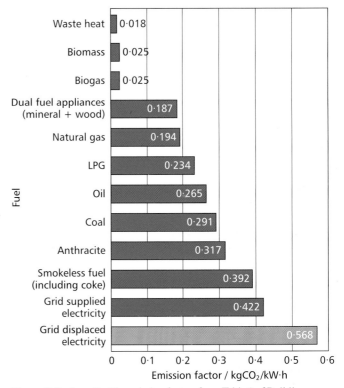

**Figure 6** Carbon dioxide emission factors from Table 2 of Building Regulations Approved Document L2A[17]

#### 3.1.7.5 Costs of LZC

Cost remains the main barrier to the installation of LZC systems. Three different measures of cost can influence decision-making on LZCs:

— capital cost per unit of generating capacity

— costs per unit of energy supplied to the building occupier

— costs per tonne of carbon emissions avoided.

Unit costs of supply and carbon abatement should ideally be calculated as whole lifecycle costs, i.e. accounting for capital, operating, and maintenance costs, and savings on grid-supplied utilities etc. It should be noted that speculative developments are not driven by lifecycle costing, but owner-occupiers will take into account running costs.

The capital costs of LZCs are very likely to be higher than alternative, traditional equipment for meeting electrical or cooling demands. However, other drivers (such as the need to satisfy planning policies or comply with building regulations) often overshadow any cost barriers to LZCs, as long as the viability of a development is not threatened.

There are grants available for certain LZCs for certain applications. For example, at the time of writing, the Department of Trade and Industry's Low Carbon Buildings Programme (http://www.lowcarbonbuildings.org.uk) provides grants for low and zero carbon technologies to householders, community organisations, schools and the public.

For more information on whole life costs refer to ISO DIS 15686-5: *Buildings and constructed assets. Service life planning*: Part 5: *Life cycle costing*[24].

In summary, the installation of LZCs is driven by the need for carbon reduction rather than capital or even whole life cost savings. The key factors when appraising and comparing LZC options become:

— the relative capital costs of different LZC options

— their relative carbon abatement costs, and

— the impact of running costs on users.

This is particularly the case when the aim is to meet a specific target for reducing $CO_2$ emissions.

### 3.1.8 LZC technology options

New developments need energy in the form of both electricity and heat. A range of low and zero carbon technologies exist that can supply electricity or heat, or both in the case of CHP (with zero carbon options broadly corresponding to what are commonly referred to as 'renewables').

The scale of development largely determines the LZC options to be considered, which fall into two broad groups:

— site-wide generators with distributed supply

— systems serving individual buildings or blocks.

Table 3 sets out the low and zero carbon technologies and the typical applications.

The feasibility and design of the technologies set out above will require serious consideration prior to a planning application being submitted. Detailed feasibility studies of the technologies should be prepared to determine which can be employed to meet a proportion of the building's energy demand.

**Table 3** Common low and zero carbon technologies and typical applications (*Note*: this table does not cover all technologies)

| Low and zero carbon technologies | Typical site-wide application | Typical individual building application |
| --- | --- | --- |
| (a) Low carbon | | |
| Gas-fired CHP | Large scale generation with district heating | Smaller scale generation for individual buildings |
| Tri-generation (gas-fired CHP plus absorption cooling) | Large scale generation with district heating and local absorption cooling | Smaller scale generation for individual buildings |
| Fuel cells (see section 5.1.5.2) | Early stage of development | Early stage of development |
| Energy from waste; advanced thermal treatments | Large scale application for sites with significant waste throughput | — |
| (b) Renewable | | |
| Solar water heating and solar air collectors | Limited application | Building-integrated technology applied to individual buildings |
| Wind turbines | Large scale wind turbines for large sites that can accommodate stand-alone turbines (e.g. 50 kW to 2 MW turbines) | Smaller scale wind turbines can be building-integrated (e.g. 1–6 kW) |
| Photovoltaics (PV) | Limited application | Building integrated photovoltaics |
| Biomass heating | Biomass community/district heating for larger scale developments | Biomass boilers for individual buildings |
| Biomass heating with absorption cooling | Biomass community/district heating and cooling for larger scale developments | — |
| Biomass combined heat and power (CHP) | Currently large scale (e.g. around 20 MWe) | Currently not well proven for small scale applications |
| Energy from waste: anaerobic digestion, gasification and pyrolysis | Large scale application for sites with significant waste throughput | — |
| Small scale hydro | Appropriate for sites with a watercourse that has a high head or a high flow | Rare as only appropriate for sites with a watercourse with high head or high flow |
| Ground source heating and cooling (considered a 'renewable' technology in the GLA renewables toolkit) | Boreholes or ground loops serving more than one building, linked with community heating/cooling | Boreholes or ground loops serving individual buildings |

Planning applications for major developments for the Greater London Authority (GLA), and some other regional planning authorities, will have to provide an energy strategy report for individual buildings (see section 3.1.1).

### 3.1.9 Low and zero carbon technologies

#### 3.1.9.1 Gas-fired CHP and tri-generation

CHP is a process involving simultaneous generation of heat and electricity, where the heat generated in the process is harnessed via heat recovery equipment for heating. When CHP is used in conjunction with absorption cooling, it is known as tri-generation.

Issues to consider for CHP and tri-generation are:

— the technical and financial viability of the system; CHP and tri-generation only save carbon dioxide and money when they are operating and require a significant base heat/cooling load to be viable

— the capital costs of installing plant

— the potential for a community CHP scheme to service a number of buildings

— the provision of an energy centre for a community CHP or tri-generation plant

— the density of the development to minimise the infrastructure costs

— the provision of appropriate plant-room space.

More guidance on CHP and tri-generation is set out in section 5.1.5.1.

#### 3.1.9.2 Energy from waste: advanced thermal treatments

Advanced thermal treatments turn waste into energy rich fuels by heating the waste under controlled conditions. These treatments are only really applicable to community-scale projects. As a guide, advanced thermal treatment plants are only economically viable for larger municipal plants having throughputs of 30 000–60 000 tonnes of waste per annum or more[25].

This technology is one of the options for disposal of non-recyclable waste discussed in section 3.9.5.

#### 3.1.9.3 Solar hot water heating and solar air collectors

These systems use energy from the sun to heat water or air using panel collectors on the roof or façade. Solar hot water heating is typically used to meet a proportion of the domestic hot water demand and solar air collectors are used for ventilation air heating and process air heating.

The technology is typically integrated into individual buildings and the following should be considered when considering the built form and layout of the site:

— orientation of the buildings or roofs: ideally, the collectors should be mounted in a south-facing location, although south-east/south-west will also function successfully

— solar access to the site and potential shading from obstacles such as buildings and trees.

For more information on these technologies, see sections 5.1.6.1 and 5.1.6.2 below.

#### 3.1.9.4 Wind turbines

In the UK, the wind provides a major renewable source for generating electricity and wind energy installations can range from small domestic turbines to large commercial wind farms.

At a community level, wind turbines can be used to generate the energy requirements of, for example, a community building (a large building or a group of buildings), perhaps selling any surplus energy to the grid. On a commercial scale, remote wind turbines measuring up to 140 m tall with capacities of over 2 MW each are used to generate electricity sold directly into the electricity grid or to users via a private wire network.

There are a range of specific issues that need to be considered for wind turbines, these include:

— *Planning issues*: such as noise, shadow flicker, visual impact, land take, impact on flight paths and radar, access roads for installation and maintenance.

— *Significant nearby obstacles*: such as tall buildings, trees or hills that are likely to reduce windspeed or increase turbulence.

— *Average wind speeds*: the British Wind Energy Association (BWEA) suggests a large wind turbine to be viable where wind speed is 7 m/s or above. An initial estimate of average wind speeds for the site can be established by using the DTI wind database, which is accessible from the BWEA website (http://www.bwea.com).

— *Distance from buildings*: particularly residential buildings. There is no official guidance on the separation to be maintained between turbines and surrounding development in terms of either minimum distances or areas. Reference should be made to the DTI's *Assessment and rating of noise from wind farms*[26] when assessing a site for planning purposes.

More guidance on wind turbines is set out in section 5.1.6.6.

#### 3.1.9.5 Photovoltaics

Photovoltaic (PV) systems convert energy from the sun into electricity through semiconductor cells. The technology is typically integrated into individual buildings and the following should be considered when designing the built form and layout of the site:

— orientation of the buildings or roofs and available area of south-facing roof and façade

— appropriate integration into roof, façade, shading devices etc.

— solar access to the site and potential shading from obstacles such as buildings and trees.

For more information on these technologies, see sections 5.1.6.1 and 5.1.6.2.

### 3.1.9.6        Biomass heating and CHP

Biomass heating involves burning a biofuel rather than a fossil fuel in a boiler.

Issues to consider for biomass heating are:

— space requirements for storage of the fuel and ash

— site access for large lorries delivering the fuel

— access to the boilers to provide the fuel

— provision of a suitable supply chain for biomass fuel.

Biomass boilers can be applied to smaller developments, to replace conventional gas-fired boilers.

Biomass-fired CHP is currently applicable for larger scale developments with steam generating plant fired by wood chips or gasification followed by gas turbine cogeneration. Small-scale biomass-fired CHP is currently in development and has been trialled in the UK.

Biomass-fired CHP offers a significant carbon saving potential for large sites (e.g. over 20 MWe). The emissions factor for biomass fuel is very low compared to fossil and other fuels. In the past, $CO_2$ emissions were assumed to be zero, ignoring the energy use for processing and transport. While biomass is still considered a renewable fuel source, Building Regulations Approved Document L2A[17] now cites a $CO_2$ emissions factor, which should be used in calculations (see Figure 6 above).

At the larger scale, biomass-fired CHP will typically use steam turbines linked to a community/district heat distribution network. At the scale of plant likely to be commercially viable, the provision of a wood chip processing facility or 'tree station' alongside the plant is likely to be considered.

Biomass CHP or heating can be used in conjunction with absorption chillers for buildings with cooling demands. Electricity demands for cooling can be reduced and converted to heat demands through the use of absorption chillers. Depending on the size of the development and the infrastructure demands, absorption cooling could be provided either by a neighbourhood plant serving a district cooling network or by building specific plant for any users with high cooling demands.

The issues to consider for biomass CHP are similar to biomass boilers, but also include:

— high capital costs of large-scale biomass CHP; joint ventures should be considered (see section 5.8)

— potential use of absorption cooling

— location of flues and heights

— location for the provision of large plant

— provision of a tree station to process biomass

More information on heating and biomass CHP is set out in sections 5.1.6.4 and 5.1.6.5.

### 3.1.9.7        Energy from waste — anaerobic digestion

Anaerobic digestion allows energy to be generated from putrescible biodegradable waste. This technology generates only small amounts of energy from a given quantity of waste and requires a large amount of waste to become viable. Collection and waste handling is complex. The quantity and mix of waste arisings from the proposed development has to be predicted and used to calculate potential energy generation.

This technology is covered in more detail in section 3.9.5.

### 3.1.9.8        Small scale hydro

This technology is used to produce electricity and it is only appropriate when there is a water course running through the site.

Depending on the water flow and head of the river different types of turbines are used. However, in economic terms, schemes with high head and low flow tend to be more convenient. It is normally most convenient in off-grid locations where the electricity produced can also be used for space and water heating. In grid-connected locations, if the site is suitable for small scale hydro, it is normally possible to produce sufficient electricity to export some to the grid.

Issues to be considered for small scale hydro:

— river flow rate

— river head

— abstraction licence issues

— space to locate plant room, pipe and reservoir (if required).

For more information see British Hydropower Association website (http://www.british-hydro.org/).

### 3.1.9.9        Ground source heating and cooling

Ground source heating and cooling uses the relatively stable low temperature (compared to the indoor setpoint) of the ground or bodies of water as a source for providing heating and cooling in buildings. There are different systems available as set out in section 5.1.6.7. The most common system is ground source heating and cooling using ground source heat pumps.

Ground source heat pumps can be used to serve more than one building when linked to a community heating scheme.

The following should be considered when appraising the suitability of ground source heating/cooling at the early stages in the design process:

— available land for horizontal ground loop

— potential low temperature uses within the buildings

— geotechnical assessment for boreholes, including hydro-geological survey information for existing boreholes; this would give an indication of potential yields in the area

— consents from the Environment Agency for open loop boreholes.

More guidance on ground source heating and cooling is set out in section 5.1.6.7.

### 3.1.10 Implications of large scale LZC

Large scale LZC options will have implications in terms of:

— the need for supporting infrastructure for energy distribution, particularly heat

— financing and management: the need for developers to engage with specialist partners in the form of energy generation and supply companies, or energy service companies

— phasing considerations on large developments that may affect the viability of technologies that rely on all phases being completed, and

— the predicted environmental impact of the proposals, which is assessed by undertaking an environmental impact assessment.

These issues are addressed in more detail below.

#### 3.1.10.1 Infrastructure

Central generation introduces the need to distribute any heat or electricity that is generated around the development. For heat, this requires a dedicated heat main. For cooling, heat can be used to drive local absorption cooling. For electricity, each unit generated must either be used on site, exported to the national grid, or dumped to waste.

Supplying locally generated electricity direct to local consumers can avoid transmission and distribution losses that occur when electricity is supplied from central power stations. For more information refer to Good Practice Guide GPG389: *Community Heating for planners and developers*[27].

#### 3.1.10.2 Financing and management

For large schemes, developers are likely to partner with an energy services company (ESCo). Their services may include supplying renewable energy and implementing energy efficiency. ESCos can finance, or assist in arranging financing, by providing a savings guarantee. They generally act as developers for their power plant and assume the associated technical and performance risks. Typically, they offer the following services:

— finance and design of energy generation and supply projects

— install and maintain the renewable energy equipment involved

— measure, monitor, and verify the project's energy savings.

More information on ESCos and multi-utility provision can be found in section 5.8.

Energy supply companies may be looking for sites to develop renewable energy supply options such as biomass power stations or wind farms in order to meet their renewables obligation. This obligation requires energy supply companies to ensure that a minimum of 10% of the electricity they supply is generated from renewable sources by 2010. There may be opportunities to locate biomass power stations close to developments to utilise the waste heat.

#### 3.1.10.3 Phasing considerations

For large developments that are to be built in phases, there are implications for some of the options. For example, an energy-from-waste plant will only become viable when there is sufficient waste generated from the proposed development to provide sufficient fuel. If this is the case, then an interim or alternative solution would be required to provide low carbon heating until a plant becomes viable.

Biomass CHP, though viable at a whole development level, could present some phasing issues in terms of integrating the heat network throughout a large development, particularly when it is likely to be phased over a number of years. However, there are already biomass plants that have been built simply to provide electricity and which are viable due to the renewable obligation and other income generated from the supply of electricity.

A plant could be built as part of the first phase of a development that initially supplied electricity only, and then progressively supplied heat as the load developed. Such a plant could potentially be developed by a specialist renewable energy company in partnership with the developers of the site. An agreement could be put in place to supply heat and electricity with the surplus electricity being sold to the grid.

New developments have potential, over time, to take heat generated from the power station which should improve the commercial viability of the site to potential utility partners, as government grants are available to companies developing large scale CHP schemes.

#### 3.1.10.4 Environmental impact assessment

Large scale LZC options, such as biomass power stations, CHP and wind farms, would require an Environmental Impact Assessment to be undertaken and it may take a long period to secure planning permission, assuming there are no fundamental barriers.

For more information about environmental impact assessments and environmental statements see section 4.5.

### 3.1.11 Enabling energy management

A metering strategy for the project should be developed to enable effective energy management. This should include heat meters for district heating systems as well as electricity meters individual buildings. The meters allow building operators to monitor where energy is actually

**Table 6** Key predicted climate changes for the medium-high emissions scenarios

| Key predicted climate change effect | Description | Implications for buildings | Example measures |
|---|---|---|---|
| General increase in temperatures | Current modal temperature in London is 10 °C; predicted to be 12 °C by 2080.<br><br>High summer temperatures will become frequent and very cold winters will become rare. | Increased outgassing of pollutants from structure and furnishings affecting indoor air quality.<br><br>Decaying waste more likely to smell and may cause problems with infestation. | Avoid high internal temperatures and VOCs in finishes, construction materials, carpets and furnishings; select labelled low emission products.<br><br>Allocate adequate space and ensure secure, sealed storage of segregated wastes in regularly cleaned area designed to avoid overheating. |
| Milder winters | Mean winter temperatures predicted to increase by 2.5 °C in SE England and 2 °C in N England. Decrease in heating degree days (cf 1980s) of 35–40% for London, 30% for Edinburgh by 2080. | Reduced energy use in winter. | Consideration should be given to the potential to reduce system capacity and thereby reduce energy use during winter months, see section 5.1.3. |
| Rising summer temperatures | Increase in mean summer temp.[31]:<br>(a) SE England: 2.5–3 °C by 2050; 4.5–5 °C by 2080<br>(b) N England and Scotland: 1.5–2 °C by 2050; 2.5–3.5 °C by 2080.<br><br>Occurrence of temp. >28 °C increases from 1–2 days/year (1989) to 20 days/year by 2080 in London. Increased occurrence of hot spells (no. of days when previous 3–5 days have >3 hours at 25 °C). Increase in cooling degree-days (cf 1989): e.g. +150–200 for London, +20–25 for Edinburgh by 2080. | Higher summertime temperatures will increase overheating risk in buildings. Due to rising external temperatures the traditional mechanism for cooling buildings through ventilation with external air cannot be relied upon. Careful design required to reduce dependence on mechanical cooling and to maintain indoor comfort. | Incorporation of intelligent ventilation systems, preferably automated, are set up to limit ventilation during warmer parts of the day and recharging 'coolth' reservoirs in high mass buildings when external air temperatures permit. |
| Enhanced urban heat island effect | In central London the urban heat island effect can currently lead to summer night time temperatures 5–6 °C warmer than temperatures in rural areas outside London. This effect is expected to intensify due to climate change, leading to a greater temperature difference between the heat island and surrounding rural areas, and more hours of night time heat island effect per year[32]. | The increase in night time urban temperature due to the urban heat island effect reduces the ability of buildings within the urban heat island to use night time cooling as a strategy Increased temperatures, particularly at night for any building within urban conurbations, reduces the ability to dissipate heat at night making night time 'free cooling' less practicable in the future. | Planting of trees, vegetation and green space for shade and natural cooling through evapotranspiration (estimated to result in 1–5 °C reduction in peak summer temperatures[33].<br><br>Green roofs (may reduce surface temperature by 20–40 °C compared to a conventional dark flat roof). |
| Wetter winters, more intense rainfall | Winters will become wetter by up to 10% across the country by the 2050s and up to 20–30% across UK by the 2080s.<br><br>In combination with higher wind speeds, occurrence of driving rain will increase in winter months. | Inability of drainage system to cope with storm surges. damage to some building materials. Increased risk of flash flooding. | Undertake flood risk assessment; design for flood resilience and to reduce flood risk. Use SUDS techniques. Locate 'resistant' uses (e.g. car parking) in high risk areas and raise ground floors.<br><br>Use of building materials which are resilient to driving rain. |
| Drier summers | Decrease in summer rainfall of 40% across most of the UK by the 2080s. Decrease in soil moisture content especially in summer: 30% decrease predicted for most of England and 10–20% for the rest of England, Wales and most of Scotland. | Increased pressure on water resources and increased occurrence of hosepipe bans. Increased pressure for water storage capacity.<br><br>Possible disruption due to increased subsidence due to drier clay soils. | Apply water efficiency principles in new and existing buildings. Plan for building operation in drought conditions. Avoid siting 'water-hungry' developments in areas prone to drought. |
| Higher daily mean winter wind speeds | Possible increase of 7% by the 2080s with the greatest increase in SE England. | Increased risk of wind damage. Higher infiltration and winter heat loss.<br><br>Pylons carrying electricity and tele-communications may be vulnerable to higher wind speeds. Increased level of power shortages and outages. | Strengthening of tall buildings, increased airtightness and incorporation of cladding materials able to cope with higher wind speeds.<br><br>Incorporation of local/on-site generation of power and renewables to reduce dependence on the grid |

discussion of climate change and the indoor environment is provided within CIBSE TM36: *Climate change and the indoor environment: impacts and adaptation*[35]. Within this study, eleven case study buildings were analysed and models were run to see how each of the buildings would perform when subjected to climate change 'as built' and also 'adapted' to improve performance. It is recommended that reference is made to this document in building design.

The key climate change issues, the implications for buildings, and considerations at the project brief and detailed design stage are summarised in Table 6. This summarises the issues set out in:

— CIBSE TM36: *Climate change and the indoor environment: impacts and adaptation*[35]

— Greater London Authority: *Adapting to climate change: a checklist for development: Guidance on designing developments in a changing climate*[36]

— Hacker JN, Belcher SE and Connell RK: *Beating the heat: keeping UK buildings cool in a warming climate*[37].

### 3.3.4 Implications

Building design in the UK has evolved to provide a comfortable internal environment in a temperate northern European climate. With the onset of climate change, the traditional mechanisms utilised in building design will require revision; there is a need for innovative thinking to find new solutions.

Thermal discomfort in summer is likely to become a major issue in the future and there will be more situations where either building occupants will have to accept, and adapt to, higher internal temperatures, or where some form of mechanical cooling will have to be provided. London and South East England will be the first to feel the impact of these changes as conventional processes previously relied upon, namely cooling by ventilating with external air, are already becoming ineffective within these areas.

Conventional mechanical cooling results in:

— additional carbon emissions from energy use, further contributing to climate change, and

— heat rejection into the local environment, which exacerbates the urban heat island effect.

The key challenge is to design buildings that reduce the requirements for mechanical cooling, as far as possible, and then to meet the remaining cooling demand with low carbon techniques such as ground coupling.

### 3.3.5 Key actions

Building services engineers should:

— consult CIBSE TM36[35] when designing building services

— give consideration to location of the development and the climate changes predicted for that location

— identify the case study building most similar to the building under design to identify the key risks to

the internal environment and adaptation mechanisms.

For further information on adapting to climate change refer to the UKCIP *Adaptation Actions* database[38] (http://www.ukcip.org.uk/resources/tools/database.asp).

## 3.4 Flood risk

In the design of a building the flood risk at that development site must be considered in addition to the potential impact that a building will have on flood risk in the surrounding catchment area. It must be recognised that, as a result of climate change an area not currently at significant risk of flooding could become so during the lifetime of the development[36].

### 3.4.1 Principles

The risk of flooding is increasing as development changes the nature of the flood plain and as the climate alters, affecting rainfall intensity and sea levels.

| The principles to apply to reduce flooding are: |
| --- |
| — avoid locations at higher risk of flooding |
| — reduce the risk of flooding |
| — avoid increasing off-site flood risks |
| — design for flood resilience where necessary. |

These principles should be applied by the project team. Examples of measures that should be applied by the building services engineer to design for flood resilience are included below.

### 3.4.2 Types of flood risk

The type of flood risk can be grouped as shown in Table 7.

Planning Policy Statement 25[39] is a key document that sets out to ensure that appropriate planning decisions are made in relation to development and flood risk. The main aims of the document are to:

— reduce the threat to people and their property, and

— deliver the greatest environmental, social and economic benefit, consistent with the government's sustainable development principles.

In order to mitigate the risk of flooding, the following should be undertaken to establish the flood risk as part of the design process at the strategic level[39]:

— *Sequential test*: a risk-based sequential test should be applied at all stages of planning as detailed in Planning Policy Statement 25[39]. The aim of the sequential test is to steer new development to areas at the lowest probability of flooding (i.e. Zone 1).

— *Exception test*: departures from the sequential approach will only be justified in exceptional circumstances, and should be tested by the exception test. The exception test provides a method of managing flood risk while still allowing necessary development to occur[39]. In this case, measures

**Table 7** Types of flood risk

| Type of flooding | Details |
| --- | --- |
| Flooding from rivers | Rivers flooding when amount of water in them exceeds the flow capacity of the river channel. |
| Flooding from sea | Flooding to low-lying land from the sea and tidal estuaries is caused by storm surges and high tides. |
| Flooding from land | Flooding from land occurs when intense rainfall is unable to soak into the ground or enter the drainage system, often this is a result of intense rainfall over a short duration. This results in local flooding. In developed areas this water can be polluted with domestic sewage. |
| Flooding from ground water | When water levels in the ground rise above surface elevations groundwater flooding occurs. This is most likely to occur in low-lying areas underlain by permeable rocks. |
| Flooding from sewers | In urban areas rainwater is frequently drained into surface water sewers or combined sewer (containing surface and waste water, known to occur in London and Portsmouth). |
| Flooding from artificial sources, e.g. reservoirs, canals, artificial lakes | Non-natural or artificial flooding can occur where water is retained above natural ground level. Reservoirs or canals can flood as a result of being overwhelmed or as a result of a dam or bank failure leading to sudden occurrence of rapidly flowing, deep water. |

would have to be applied to the proposed development to manage the flood risk.

The types of flood risk assessment and the order in which they should be undertaken is set out in Planning Policy Statement 25[39].

The flood risk zones are defined in Planning Policy Statement 25 and can be summarised as follows:

— *Zone 1: Low Probability*: comprises land assessed as having a less than 1 in 1000 chance of river and sea flooding in any year (<0.1%).

— *Zone 2: Medium Probability*: comprises land assessed as having between a 1 in 100 and a 1 in 1000 chance of river flooding (1.0–0.1%) and between a 1 in 200 and a 1 in 1000 chance of sea flooding (0.5–0.1%) in any year.

— *Zone 3a: High Probability*: This zone comprises land assessed as having a 1 in 100 or greater chance of river flooding (>1%) and a 1 in 200 or greater chance of flooding from the sea (>0.5%) in any year.

— *Zone 3b: The Functional Floodplain*: comprises land where water has to flow or be stored in times of flood.

### 3.4.3 Example measures

At the site level the aim is to reduce the effect of development by managing surface water in a sustainable manner to enable the following targets to be achieved:

— the developed site should achieve levels of surface water leaving the site equal to that of the undeveloped site, i.e. achieve 'green field' run-off rates

— reduce flood risk to site itself

— reduce risk to other parts of the catchment area.

Managing flood risk at the site level can be achieved through the measures summarised in Table 8 and Figure 8.

**Table 8** Measures for managing flood risk

| Measure | Example |
| --- | --- |
| Sustainable drainage systems (SUDS) | Filter strips and swales (vegetated areas that hold and drain water downhill mimicking natural drainage patterns. |
| Zoning of the development | Identify areas within the site for flood storage and safe water flow paths within the development layout. |
| | Figure 8 illustrates zoning techniques that can be used to reduce flood risk. |

Flood-resilient buildings are designed to reduce the consequences of flooding and facilitate recovery from the effects of flooding sooner than conventional buildings. There are a number of measures[39] that can be applied to buildings that could experience limited water penetration. These measures could not be applied to severe inundation of flood water. Some example measures are shown in Table 9.

Flooding can cause severe damage to properties. Flood water may enter properties by a variety of routes, see Figure 9.

### 3.4.3 Key actions

The building services engineer should recommend that the project team establishes the flood risk of a proposed development. In particular, it is important to consult with the local authority to establish whether a strategic flood risk assessment has been undertaken and to check with the Environment Agency.

Sustainable urban drainage systems should be employed, where feasible, see section 3.5 for more information.

Building services engineers should aim to incorporate flood resistant measures into the design of building

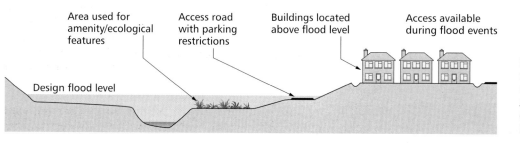

Area used for amenity/ecological features

Access road with parking restrictions

Buildings located above flood level

Access available during flood events

Design flood level

**Figure 8** Measures for managing flood risk (reproduced from CIRIA C624: *Development and Flood Risk — Guidance for the Construction Industry*[40]; CIRIA, London 2004)

**Table 9** Measures for flood resilient buildings (adapted from *Development and flood risk — guidance for the construction industry*[40])

| Measure | Details |
| --- | --- |
| Raising floor level | One method of reducing flood risk to a development is to raise the floor level of buildings to above flood defence level. Car parking and utility areas may be located at lower levels. |
| | Special consideration should be given to safety if access to floor levels that are below flood defence level is to be provided by lifts. Lifts should be prevented from operating on such floors during flood events. |
| | Basements should not be included within the design of developments within areas at risk of flooding, unless basement areas have barriers installed to keep water out of the building and access is only provided from above flood defence level. |
| Flood proofing | Flood proofing is where buildings are designed to withstand the effects of flooding. CIRIA[40] details the following main categories of flood proofing: 'dryproofing' (flood boards or other temporary barriers to keep water out of the building), and 'wet proofing' (to improve the ability of the building to withstand the effects of flooding, once water has entered the building). |
| External walls | Careful consideration of materials. Use low permeability materials to limit water penetration if dry proofing required. Avoid using timber frame and cavity walls. Consider applying a water resistant coating. Provide fittings for flood boards or other temporary barriers across openings in the walls (dry proofing). |
| Internal walls | Avoid use of gypsum plaster and plasterboard; use more flood resistant linings (e.g. hydraulic lime, ceramic tiles). Avoid use of stud partition walls. |
| Floors | Avoid use of chipboard floors. Use concrete floors with integrated and continuous damp proof membrane and damp proof course. Solid concrete floors are preferable; if a suspended floor is to be used, provide facility for drainage of sub-floor void. Use non-porous insulation materials. |
| Fittings, fixtures and services | If possible, locate all fittings, fixtures and services above design flood level. Avoid chipboard and MDF. Consider use of removable plastic fittings. Use solid doors treated with waterproof coatings. Avoid using double-glazed window units that may fill with flood water. Use solid wood staircases. Avoid fitted carpets. Locate electrical, gas and telephone equipment and systems above design flood level. Fit anti-flooding devices to drainage systems. |
| Flood-resistant construction | Flood-resistant construction can prevent entry of water or minimise the amount of water that may enter a building where there is flooding outside. Examples include barriers to doorways. Of key consideration must be that these measures are maintained in a good state by building occupiers. |
| | (The role of flood resilient and resistant construction is being appraised and, if reliable methods can be developed, they may become part of the Building Regulations.) |
| Flood warnings | Warning and evacuation arrangements including acceptable safe access and egress arrangements should be made for frequent and extreme floods. |

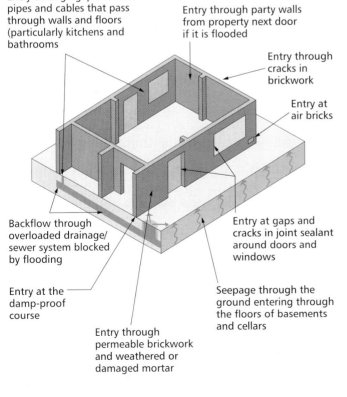

**Figure 9** Flood water penetration into a residential property (reproduced from CIRIA C624: *Development and flood risk — guidance for the construction industry*[40]; CIRIA, London 2004)

Labels in figure:
- Entry through gaps around pipes and cables that pass through walls and floors (particularly kitchens and bathrooms
- Entry through party walls from property next door if it is flooded
- Entry through cracks in brickwork
- Entry at air bricks
- Entry at gaps and cracks in joint sealant around doors and windows
- Seepage through the ground entering through the floors of basements and cellars
- Backflow through overloaded drainage/ sewer system blocked by flooding
- Entry at the damp-proof course
- Entry through permeable brickwork and weathered or damaged mortar

services and work with the project team to raise awareness of flood risk and flood resistance.

For further information see the following publications:

— Communities and Local Government: *Consultation on Planning Policy Statement 25: Development and Flood Risk — A summary of responses*[41] (2006)

— Communities and Local Government: *Development and Flood Risk: A Practice Guide Companion to PPS25 'Living Draft'*[42] (2007)

— CIRIA: *Development and Flood Risk — Guidance for the Construction Industry*[40] (2004)

— CIRIA: *The SUDS Manual*[43] (2007)

— CIRIA: *Site handbook for the construction of SUDS*[44] (2007).

## 3.5　Sustainable drainage strategy

Sustainable drainage systems (SUDS) is an approach to managing rainfall that aims to mimic natural drainage and avoid the problems associated with conventional drainage (flooding and pollution). It is a concept that includes long term environmental and social factors in decisions about drainage.

Sustainable drainage systems should be integrated with systems such as rainwater harvesting and wastewater treatment. The main relationship between SUDS and building services engineering is through the integration with rainwater collection systems.

### 3.5.1 Principles

SUDS is about managing run-off. When rainfall occurs faster than water can infiltrate into the ground it becomes surface run-off.

> The principles to apply relating to sustainable drainage are:
>
> — reduce run-off from the site
>
> — attenuate run-off from the site (see Figure 10)
>
> — exploit or enhance existing natural drainage systems and/or techniques modelled on them
>
> — provide additional benefits (amenity, habitats, etc.)

These principles would be applied by the project team, in particular the drainage engineer and the landscape architect. The Environment Agency may set requirements for sites to reduce run-off as part of a sustainable drainage strategy or to contribute towards mitigating flood risk (see section 3.4).

On greenfield sites a relatively low percentage of rainfall flows from the surface to watercourses such as rivers or streams. The presence of grass and other vegetation slows down the surface flow to the watercourses. When sites are developed and the amount of impervious surfaces (e.g. roofs and roads) increases infiltration, evapotranspiration and the amount of vegetation are reduced.

The aim of SUDS is to return the post-development run-off, infiltration and evapotranspiration to as near natural conditions as possible, thereby minimising the adverse effects of urbanisation on the water environment.

### 3.5.2 Example measures

The techniques used in SUDS can be grouped into four general methods of control:

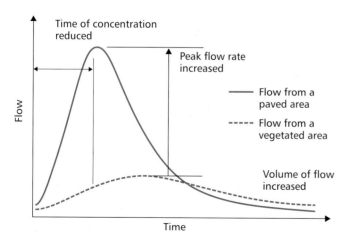

**Figure 10** Graph showing attenuation of water run-off (reproduced from CIRIA C522: *Sustainable urban drainage systems — design manual for England and Wales*[45]; CIRIA, London 2000)

— filter strips and swales

— filter drains and permeable surfaces

— infiltration devices

— basins, ponds and wetlands.

These techniques are illustrated in Figure 11.

Permeable surfaces include the use of permeable paving which provides hard standing with a porous surface, allowing rainwater to pass through. There are a number of variations on these techniques and recent innovations includes green roofs, geo-cellular box storage and bio-retention structures.

Sites with high run-off rates can use attenuation to reduce the flows. This can be carried out by using storage to hold back excessive volume using tanks or oversized pipes with the flow controlled downstream.

Building Regulations Approved Document H[46], states that infiltration of run-off is preferred over discharge to watercourses. Discharge to sewers should be used only when no other option is available.

### 3.5.3 Integrating SUDS and rainwater collection

Sustainable drainage systems may incorporate storage for re-use of rainwater.

The permanent storage volume for rainwater collection systems will generally have to be additional to any storage volume required to control run-off rates, unless a continuous rate of use for the rainwater can be guaranteed. This is to avoid the risk that the rainwater collection tank is already full when it is required to provide storage for attenuation of storm water.

Further information on the design of systems for rainwater reuse is provided in section 5.2.6.

### 3.5.4 SUDS and living roofs

Roofs are one of the most significant contributors to rainfall run-off in drainage systems. Living roofs (often referred to as 'green' or 'brown' roofs) can be used to reduce the volume and rate of run-off. Living roofs are rooftops planted with vegetation and provide habitat for insects and birds. There are two main types of living roof:

— *intensive living roofs*: have a deep layer of soil

— *extensive living roofs*: lightweight, often with shallower growing material.

Intensive green roofs are most appropriate for use in SUDS, as they have more capacity to store rainwater run-off and so reduce the rate of run-off, see Figure 12. More information on living roofs can be found in section 3.7.3.

Green roofs remove leaves and roof litter from run-off and also reduce pollutant load from roofs. They also filter out any heavy metals present on the roof from atmospheric fallout. Living roofs also help in reducing the urban heat island effect, see section 3.7.4.

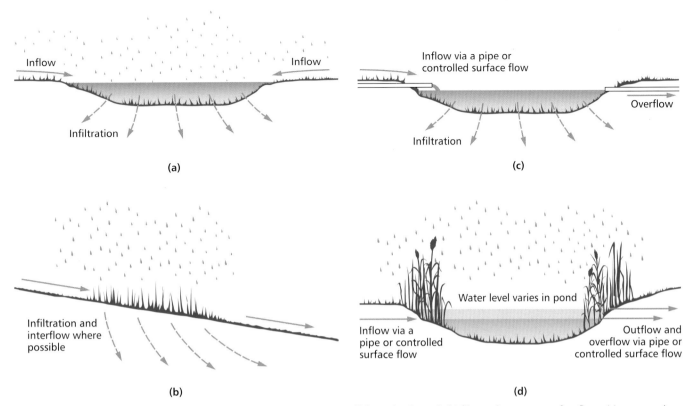

**Figure 11** Sustainable urban drainage techniques; (a) swales to convey run-off along the channel, (b) filter strips to treat surface flows, (c) cross-section through an infiltration basis, (d) pond inflow and outflow (reproduced from CIRIA C522: *Sustainable urban drainage systems — design manual for England and Wales*[45]; CIRIA, London 2000)

### 3.5.5    Key actions

Selection and design of sustainable drainage systems are multidisciplinary processes. Landscape architects and drainage engineers will have to work closely together to provide a successful strategy. The project team should consult with the Environment Agency (or the appropriate authority) to determine the requirements for reducing run-off from the site.

There are a wide range of factors to consider when designing sustainable drainage systems. Unlike conventional drainage systems, factors that influence the final choice will include planning, water quality, water resource, architectural and landscape requirements. For example, the following would have to be determined:

— rainfall data

— soil type and infiltration potential

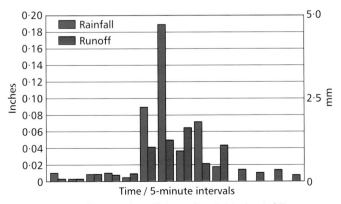

**Figure 12** Run-off attenuation efficiency for a 0.4-inch rainfall event with saturated media (source: US Environmental Protection Agency: *Vegetated roof cover*[47])

— environmental sensitivity of site

— availability and cost of land

— amenity provision

— ecology and wildlife habitat provision

— health and safety considerations.

Unlike conventional drainage systems, sustainable drainage systems may not be formally adopted by the local water authority. Therefore, responsibility for the provision, operation and maintenance of sustainable drainage systems is often a barrier to their successful implementation.

The following publications provide further information and guidance:

— CIRIA: *Sustainable drainage systems — hydraulic, structural and water quality advice*[48] (2004)

— HR Wallingford: *Use of SUDS in high density developments — guidance manual*[49] (2005)

— CIRIA: *Sustainable drainage systems — design manual for England and Wales*[45] (2000)

## 3.6    Transport strategy

Transport accounts for almost a quarter of $CO_2$ emissions in the UK and contributes to poor air quality.

A sustainable transport strategy should improve accessibility and safety for all modes of travel, particularly for alternatives to the car such as walking, cycling and public transport.

### 3.6.1    Principles

> The principles to apply relating to sustainable transport are:
> — reducing use of the private car
> — encouraging walking and cycling
> — encouraging the use of public transport
> — encouraging provision of information on sustainable modes of transport

These principles would be applied by the project team, in particular the transport consultant. The local authority may have requirements for sustainable transport based on its planning policies.

For larger developments, a transport assessment would have to be undertaken. A transport assessment is a comprehensive and systematic process that sets out transport issues relating to a proposed development.

In some cases, the transportation issues arising out of development proposals may not require a full transport assessment to adequately inform the process and identify suitable mitigation. In these instances, a simplified report in the form of a transport statement (TS) may be expected. There will also be situations where the transport issues relating to a development proposal are limited, and no formal assessment is necessary.

More information about transport assessments and statements is set out in the Department for Transport's *Guidance for Transport Assessment*[50] and indicative thresholds for when a transport assessment is required are set out in Appendix B of this guidance.

A transport assessment would address the following:

— the accessibility of the site for all forms of transport

— the predicted number of trips that the development will generate and their impact on the transport network

— the likely split between forms of transport used to reach and leave the site

— the measures proposed to improve access, especially for forms of transport other than the car

— road access and safety, pedestrian access and safety, cycling, public transport and parking

— impact of the development on the local and wider highway network, including any junction capacity issues

— inclusive access for all users.

Sustainable transport is encouraged by the development of a site-specific travel plan. A travel plan is a package of measures produced by employers to encourage staff to use alternatives to single-occupancy car-use. The measures contained within travel plans can help in reducing congestion and air pollution from developments.

### 3.6.2    Example measures

A sustainable transport strategy would include a range of measures that rely on how the proposed development will operate. There are a number of measures that can be applied at the site planning stage and as part of the building layout and design.

#### 3.6.2.1    *Reducing use of the private car*

Measures which may assist in reducing car usage, particularly single occupancy vehicles include car sharing/pooling, high occupancy vehicle lanes and parking control.

A car club can be set up as a joint venture with an established vehicle rental or car club company. Car clubs are often set up for projects that include residential developments. There is no minimum number of units to support a car station if the development is within a wider car club scheme. Standalone car clubs within a single development are not ideal, but could be possible with a development of 250 residential units or more.

All of the vehicles should be low emission vehicles using electrical, hybrid or LPG and eventually fuel cell vehicles. Potentially, electric vehicles can be charged via the development's own CHP/solar/wind power units.

#### 3.6.2.2    *Walking and cycling*

Secure cycle parking should be provided at convenient locations close to entrances of the buildings and the site should be linked to existing cycle routes through the provision of additional cycle lanes.

Pedestrian routes should be identified and provided, with clear 'wayfinding' signs and pedestrian crossings for safety. The walking and cycling routes should consider the desire likely routes that people will walk when lines linking the proposed development with going to and from public transport nodes and surrounding facilities.

#### 3.6.2.3    *Public transport*

Patronage of bus services to a local transport node, such as a railway station has to be promoted. Design of the development should encourage easy access to existing public transport facilities, such as bus stops. For larger developments, the provision of dedicated bus stops should be considered.

#### 3.6.2.4    *Increasing accessibility*

Developments should be designed to promote access for all via a variety of transport modes. They should be designed with safety and security in mind. Some of these measures would be the provision of:

— good quality lighting of all public areas (whilst limiting light pollution)

— tactile paving and surfaces suitable for all pedestrians

— low floor buses

— disabled parking spaces located next to suitable lifts etc.

— car parks to be designed to exceed current Secure Car Park standards (http://www.securedcarparks.com)

— clear and concise signage.

### 3.6.3 Key actions

Once the scale of development has been determined it will be necessary to liaise with transport planners, in order to identify the scope of transportation work required by the local authority.

If a transport assessment is required, this will need to be prepared prior to the submission of a planning application. It can be possible to agree to prepare the 'heads of terms' of a travel plan prior to submission of a planning application, which agrees the principle of the travel plan. The travel plan must then be completed and agreed with the local authority prior to occupation of the development.

Building services engineers may be involved in the provision of:

— services related to the secure car parking services (http://www.securedcarparks.com)

— provision of charge-points for electric cars

— cyclists' showering and changing facilities

— provision of lighting to help promote inclusive access to developments.

For more information see the following publications:

— Department for Transport: *A guide on travel plans for developers*[51] (2005)

— Department for Communities and Local Government and Department for Transport: *Guidance for Transport Assessment*[50] (2007)

— CarPlus: *Car clubs in property developments — an information pack for developers and local authorities*[52] (2006)

## 3.7 Ecology strategy

The ecological strategy should protect existing ecological value and enhance the biodiversity of the site.

### 3.7.1 Principles

The principles to apply when developing an ecological strategy are:

— preserve and enhance site ecology

— increase the number and populations of species

— provide new and enhanced habitats

— compensate for any unavoidable loss of biodiversity.

Refer to the CIBSE on-line sustainable engineering tool[2] for practical measures and sources of guidance for each of these principles (http://www.cibse.org/sustain).

These principles can be applied by the project team, with advice from a suitably qualified ecologist. Many of these principles would be taken forward by the landscape architects and the architect.

Protection and enhancement is relevant to the local area through consultation with the local biodiversity action plan, and appropriate consideration of the impacts of anticipated climate change.

Table 10 explains the key principles in more detail.

**Table 10** Incorporating ecological features (source: London Development Agency: *Design for biodiversity*[53])

| Objectives | Comments |
|---|---|
| Retain, enhance or create features of nature conservation value and avoid harm | The design of all developments should look to incorporate and enhance the features of existing nature conservation value on, or adjacent to, a site. |
| Mitigate for impacts to features of nature conservation value | Mitigation should be considered where it is impossible to avoid all impacts to a feature of value, and also where impacts can be lessened through a change in the design or operation of a development. |
| Compensation for the loss of features of nature conservation value | Where there is no viable alternative, there should be compensation for the loss of a feature of nature conservation value. When considering compensation for habitat loss, the aim should always be to replace 'like for like' or better. |

### 3.7.2 Example measures

Specific measures to be included in the proposed development will depend on the local conditions. However, for large sites 'green infrastructure' should be considered. Green infrastructure is the sub-regional network of protected sites, nature reserves, green spaces, and greenway linkages. The linkages include river corridors and flood plains, migration routes and features of the landscape, which are of importance as wildlife corridors.

For individual buildings, the following types of features can be incorporated:

— living roofs

— bird and bat boxes

— wildlife ponds and other habitats

— selection of native species.

Habitats can be created on walls, balconies, roof terraces and decks. For example, habitats can be created for birds, insects and small mammals using climbing plants to create 'green walls'. These plants can also help to provide some shading of the walls. New buildings tend to reduce the amount of potential nesting sites, so artificial sites for bats and birds need to be provided.

### 3.7.3 Living roofs

Living roofs (often referred to as 'green' or 'brown' roofs) are rooftops planted with vegetation and can provide habitat for insects and birds.

There are two main types of living roofs:

— *Intensive living roofs*: a deep layer of soil (up to 1.5 metres) to support a variety of plants such as flowers and shrubs, but requiring regular maintenance. Intensive roof gardens can grow a range of plants, even trees and shrubs can provide a rich habitat for wildlife.

— *Extensive living roofs*: lightweight, often with shallower growing material, requiring little maintenance (e.g. mosses, sedums, grasses, succulents and herbs). The type of growing medium chosen affects the type of habitat created, which may reflect the building's surroundings. This type of roof is sometimes also known as a brown roof although not all extensive roofs, e.g. sedum roofs, are brown.

Table 11 sets out the key advantages and disadvantages for the two types of roof.

**Table 11** Comparison between intensive and extensive green roofs (source: Town and Country Planning Association: *Biodiversity by design: a guide for sustainable communities*[54])

| Type | Advantages | Disadvantages |
|---|---|---|
| Intensive (deep soil, irrigation system, more favourable conditions for plants) | Allows greater plant/habitat diversity | Heavy |
| | | Requires irrigation and drainage |
| | Good insulation properties | Higher cost |
| | Simulates wildlife garden | |
| | Diverse utilisation of roof | |
| Extensive (thin soil, little or no irrigation stressful conditions for plants) | Lightweight | Limited choice of plants |
| | Suitable for large areas and 0–30° slope | Usually no access for recreation |
| | Low maintenance | |
| | More natural | |
| | Often does not require irrigation and drainage | |

Brown roofs are examples of extensive living roofs. They are cheaper than green roofs and relatively low maintenance. They make use of materials available on the site and provide habitats similar to brownfield sites.

As well as the ecological value, living roofs have a number of benefits, such as:

— providing amenity value

— attenuating water run-off (see 3.5.4)

— providing additional thermal insulation

— providing a cooling effect

— mitigating urban heat island effect.

### 3.7.4    Living roofs and cooling effect

Buildings will benefit from reduced cooling load if their roof is planted potentially reducing the need for mechanical cooling[55]. Living roofs improve the thermal performance in both summer and winter. For example, vegetation can reduce wind chill by acting as a wind break, thus aiding heat conservation in the winter[56]. During summer, buildings with green roofs are often cooler than those with other surface treatments. Much less heat gain is observed on vegetated roofs than bare roofs, partially caused by plant shading and absorption of the sun's radiation during photosynthesis[57]. Bare surfaces act as heat sinks and vegetation does not absorb as much heat as concrete. Vegetation also cools the ambient air by consuming solar heat and using it for transpiration and photosynthesis. This cooling may also reduce the temperature of the floors below the roof, reducing any air conditioning requirements.

Vegetation placed around buildings, such as trees and climbing plants on walls, serves to reduce the surface temperature through direct shading of hard surfaces.

Living roofs can effectively help reduce the urban heat island effect in a number of ways. In particular, vegetation transpires water into the atmosphere which has a favourable cooling and humidifying effect. Vegetated surfaces have lower radiant temperatures than other hard surfaces with the same reflectivity.

For further information on living roofs, see:

— Grant G: *Green roofs and facades*[58] (2006)

— British Council for Offices: *Green roofs*[59] (2003).

### 3.7.5    Key actions

For all sites it is important to involve a suitably qualified ecologist to undertake an ecological appraisal of the site. The appraisal should include ecological survey data, with both relevant desk and field studies carried out at an appropriate time of year. According to the Institute of Environmental Management and Assessment (IEMA) (1997), 'phase 1' surveys can be undertaken all year round, to support and verify the findings of the desk-top survey, although certain protected species surveys need to be undertaken during particular seasons.

The ecological appraisal should provide recommendations on protection, enhancement and management of biodiversity on the site (both in the design of the buildings and the landscaping elements) and if necessary or justified, mitigation.

Special attention should be given to assessing the impact on nearby protected sites and taking account of the unavoidable climate change anticipated in the locality over the lifetime of the development.

For further information refer to:

— Town and Country Planning Association (TCPA): *Biodiversity by design — A guide for sustainable communities*[54] (2004)

— London Development Agency: *Design for biodiversity*[53]

## 3.8 Health and wellbeing

Health and wellbeing includes the provision of a healthy and comfortable internal environment and to provide an accessible and inclusive environment.

### 3.8.1 Principles

The principles to apply to health and wellbeing are:

— discharge all statutory health and safety obligations

— apply good practice in providing for the widest practical range of accessibility needs

— avoid and reduce health risk factors

— provide comfortable internal conditions

Refer to the CIBSE online sustainable engineering tool[(2)] for practical measures and sources of guidance for each of these principles (www.cibse.org/sustain).

These principles would be applied by the project team and the last principle, in particular, would be applied by the building services engineer.

Many of the issues relating to a healthy and comfortable internal environment are considered as more detailed design issues and are addressed in section 5.4. At the early design stage, the key issue is the provision of an accessible and inclusive environment.

### 3.8.2 Access and inclusion

An accessible and inclusive environment within the built realm is a fundamental design aim for any development. Design and access statements are now a requirement of all planning applications. The statements must demonstrate that access requirements for people with special needs and the principles of inclusive design have been fully considered, and provide details of how they are intended to be met.

The requirements that have to be addressed by developments are as follows:

— undertake an independent 3rd party accessibility audit of the design

— consider 'Lifetime Homes' standards (http://www.lifetimehomes.org.uk/)

— consult with local accessibility groups and incorporate recommendations, and

— comply with Building Regulations Approved Document M: *Access to and use of buildings*[(60)].

### 3.8.3 Key actions

The actions for building services engineers would be to incorporate the measures identified by the accessibility audit. Practical measures for access and inclusion are included in the CIBSE online sustainable engineering tool[(2)] (www.cibse.org/sustain).

For further information refer to:

— Greater London Authority: *Accessible London: achieving an inclusive environment*[(61)] (2004)

— Communities and Local Government: *Planning and access for disabled people: A Good Practice Guide*[(62)] (2003)

— *Lifetime Homes*[(63)] (http://www.lifetimehomes.org.uk/).

## 3.9 Waste strategy

Sustainable waste management should reduce the production of waste arising from the operation of buildings to a minimum. Disposal should be considered a last resort.

The principles to apply to manage waste are:

— reduce waste

— reuse materials and equipment (and facilitate future reuse)

— recycle waste (and facilitate recycling)

— compost biodegradable waste

— recover energy from waste (and facilitate energy recovery from waste).

Refer to the CIBSE online sustainable engineering tool[(2)] for practical measures and sources of guidance for each of these principles (www.cibse.org/sustain).

These principles are shown in the hierarchy of waste management as set out in BS 5906: *Waste management in buildings. Code of practice*[(64)].

### 3.9.2 Developing a waste management strategy

The following approach should be taken to preparing a waste management strategy:

— *Predict waste arisings*: examples of typical waste arisings are provided in BS 5906[(64)] and chapter 4 of CIBSE Guide G[(65)].

— *Consider relevant legislation*: see CIBSE Guide G[(65)] and BS 5906[(64)].

— *Consider the composition of waste*: chapter 4 of CIBSE Guide G[(65)] provides information on the breakdown of types of waste arisings, see Table 12 below.

— *Predict potential reduction in waste arisings*: through waste reduction schemes, reuse, recycling etc.

— *Determine feasibility of recovery options*: such as composting and energy from waste.

— *Calculate the storage, containment and equipment requirements for effective waste management*: the following should be considered: volume and composition of waste, frequency of collection, degree of waste segregation required.

This should all be undertaken along with liaison between planning authorities and architects, as well as collection authorities to ensure that proposals tie-in with local authority reclamation and recycling schemes.

**Table 12** Typical bulk and composition of commercial waste (reproduced from CIBSE Guide G[65])

| | Typical bulk density / kg·m⁻³ | Composition of waste / (% by mass) | | | | |
|---|---|---|---|---|---|---|
| | | Multiple retail outlets | Department stores | Supermarkets | Hotels | Offices |
| Folded newspaper, packed or baled cardboard; loosely crumpled paper, office stationery; wastepaper (loose in sacks) | 500 | 81 | 65 | 50 | 8 | 80 |
| Mixed general refuse, similar to domestic (no solid fuel residues) | 150 | 13 | 31 | 40 | 55 | 16 |
| Separated food waste, uncompacted vegetable waste or well compacted, moist pig swill | 200 | 4 | 2 | — | 33 | 4 |
| Salvaged bones and fat | 600 | 2 | 2 | 10 | — | — |
| Empty bottles | 300 | — | — | — | 4 | — |

### 3.9.3 Facilitating reducing, reusing and recycling of waste

The ability to reduce, reuse and recycle waste generated from buildings during operation is dependent on the occupiers and the building management. There are a range of measures that can be applied when designing buildings to facilitate waste reduction and these need to accord with the likely waste management strategy for the development.

There are various methods of sorting and separating waste for large developments. These are:

— *Sorting at source*: by the householder or commercial business into segregated bins.

— *Sorting at collection*: particularly for domestic waste where dry recyclables can be segregated by collection staff into separate bins in the waste collection vehicle.

— *Self-bring sites*: where householders and small commercial businesses can bring their waste to a central location to be disposed of into separate skips.

— *Centralised sorting*: at a municipal recycling facility (MRF), where manual and mechanical sorting techniques are employed to segregate a mixed waste input.

The more mixed a waste stream is, the greater the cost of the sorting process. It should also be noted that manual sorting of mixed waste creates a number of health and safety concerns that should be avoided.

Any waste collection strategy adopted must conform and link with the relevant local authority waste strategy, which will be entirely site-specific.

For large sites, a municipal recycling facility can be provided to enable the separation and storage of all recyclable waste collected across the site. Such a facility

allows the separation of mixed recyclables into individual materials prior to despatch to reprocessors for cleaning and preparation for manufacture into new recycled products. On-site reprocessing facilities such as baling, compaction and sorting of materials can be provided to reduce impacts of transporting off site. CIBSE Guide G[65] provides more information about the design of these facilities. Such a reprocessing facility would need to be sited away from the centre of the development but where it is easily accessible to collection vehicles whilst minimising noise impacts on surrounding areas.

A number of different measures can be applied to sites and buildings to encourage separation and recycling, such as:

— *Recycling storage facilities*: for each building to allow each occupier to be charged separately for the waste they generate. This should provide sufficient space for separate bins for each waste stream (e.g. paper, card, plastics, glass, compostable waste etc.).

— *Provision of different sizes and numbers of bins*: for different occupiers, depending on waste generation, to encourage occupiers to reduce waste and recycle as much as possible.

— *Provision of on-site composting facilities*: such as in-vessel composters (see below).

### 3.9.4 Composting

A number of different composting technologies can be used to decompose garden waste into a usable product. Some of these processes may also treat kitchen wastes. However, due to the potential risks to animal and human health from the transfer of diseases from meat wastes into the environment, there are stricter controls over the processing of kitchen type wastes and only certain approved treatments may be used for this purpose. These controls are specified by the Animal By-Products (England) Regulations 2003[66], which are regulated by Animal Health (http://www.defra.gov.uk/animalhealth).

Composting processes for municipal waste management primarily fall into two categories:

— *Windrow composting*: an established technique for dealing with garden wastes in the UK, where the material is shredded and then piled in elongated rows, called windrows, and aerated either through turning of the windrows or by forcing air through the material. Windrow composting may take place in buildings or externally.

— *In-vessel composting (IVC)*: this embraces a variety of techniques whereby kitchen and garden wastes may be composted in an enclosed vessel or tunnel. The advantage of these processes is that they are more controlled and can be designed to achieve and maintain specified temperatures to facilitate bacteria destruction in accordance with the requirements of the Animal By-Products (England) Regulations 2003[66].

Commercial composting is not economically attractive, but it can still provide a useful waste management option as it considerably reduces the volume of waste arising.

### 3.9.5 Recovering energy from waste

In any waste management strategy where a combustion technology is utilised to recover energy from waste, there will inevitably be a compromise between the widely accepted need to implement the five stage approach of the waste hierarchy (see principles in section 3.9.1) and the need to maximise energy recovery from the combustion plant and to ensure its operation is economically viable.

Mass combustion technologies are often described as 'waste hungry' and sometimes appear to oppose the hierarchal approach that reduction, re-use, recycling and recovery should all be considered preferential to end disposal.

There are various methods of disposing of non-recyclable waste. These include anaerobic digestion and advanced thermal treatments (pyrolysis and gasification).

These treatments are only really applicable to community-scale projects. As a guide, pyrolysis and gasification plants are only economically viable for municipal plants dealing with throughputs of 30 000–60 000 tonnes of waste per annum[67].

There are a number of options for disposing of waste and producing energy from the process. The key technologies are set out below.

#### 3.9.5.1 Anaerobic digestion

Anaerobic digestion is an established process for treating organic waste residues. It is used in the UK for digestion of sewage and agricultural sludges.

Anaerobic digestion works on the principle of micro-biological degradation of organic material and waste in the absence of oxygen. It is essentially the same process which takes place within a landfill site, but can be managed to a much greater extent.

60% of the waste can be converted into biogas — the rate of breakdown depends on the nature of the waste and the operating temperature. The biogas has a calorific value typically between 50% and 70% that of natural gas and can be combusted directly in modified natural gas boilers or used to run internal combustion engines. Apart from biogas, the process also produces a digestate which may be separated into liquid and solid components. The liquid is fertiliser and the solid is organic compost.

The advantages of anaerobic digestion are as follows:

— there is a significant reduction of waste in a clean process with useful end products

— the process deals with a waste stream that cannot be recycled or reused; there is no conflict with waste hierarchy.

The disadvantages are that the technology generates only small amounts of energy and collection and waste handling are complex and costly. There is also a risk of smells during use and when waste is handled.

Anaerobic digestion is an excellent technology for treating biodegradable organic waste. A future attraction of anaerobic digestion is the opportunity to integrate it with gasification (see 3.9.5.2 below).

#### 3.9.5.2 Advanced thermal treatments

Advanced thermal treatments include pyrolysis and gasification. These technologies turn waste into energy rich fuels by heating the waste under controlled conditions. Whereas incineration fully converts the input waste into energy and ash, these processes deliberately limit the conversion so that combustion does not take place directly. Instead, they convert the waste into valuable intermediates that can be further processed for materials recycling or energy recovery. The two technologies are:

— *pyrolysis*: the thermal degradation of waste in the absence of oxygen to produce char, pyrolysis oil and syngas, e.g. the conversion of wood to charcoal.

— *gasification*: the breakdown of hydrocarbons into a syngas by carefully controlling the amount of oxygen present, e.g. the conversion of coal into town gas.

The major advantage of pyrolysis is the recovery of useful by-products (such as metals or chemicals), energy recovery being a marginal benefit.

The important attraction of gasification compared with mass burn incineration is the opportunity for high-efficiency electricity generation. Where anaerobic digestion is operated alongside gasification there is an opportunity to burn the biogas with the syngas from the gasifier in the same gas turbine.

These technologies are currently unproven on a commercial scale in the UK, and overseas experience is patchy[67].

More information on these technologies can be found in:

— Department for Environment, Food and Rural Affairs: *Options for the diversion of biodegradable municipal waste from landfill*[67] (2005)

— Biffaward/C-Tech Innovation: *Thermal methods of municipal waste treatment* (Biffaward)[68] (2003).

An example of the information available in these references is shown in Table 13. The table is extracted from *Thermal methods of municipal waste treatment*[68] and shows comparative energy content of various fuels and waste.

**Table 13** Comparative values and energy content of fuel and waste (source: *Thermal methods of municipal waste treatment*[68])

| Fuel/waste type | Energy content |
|---|---|
| Coal | 6960 kW·h/tonne |
| Natural gas | 10.833 kW·h/N·m$^3$ |
| Oil | 11667 kW·h/tonne |
| Newspaper | 5154 kW·h/tonne |
| Quality paper | 5154 kW·h/tonne |
| Municipal solid waste | 2575 kW·h/tonne |
| Mixed plastic | 9585 kW·h/tonne |

### 3.9.6 Key actions

The key actions are:

— to prepare a comprehensive waste management strategy to determine how best to reduce waste arisings from the operation of the buildings

— to ensure that waste facilities are properly accommodated and serviced

— to consider the potential for energy from waste systems for developments with large volumes of waste.

Waste management issues are likely to have a major impact on the layout and function of any residential or non-residential development. To ensure that storage space for the efficient management of waste and recyclable material is incorporated into the layout it is essential that liaison between planning authorities and architects, as well as collection authorities, takes place.

The project team should reach agreement with all appropriate authorities, particularly upon the following points:

— methods of storage, segregation, on-site treatment and collection of waste, including recyclable material, to be used for the form of layout and building density adopted

— a designated location for waste including recyclable material storage, segregation and treatment areas to be provided and means of access to them for waste collection staff and vehicles

— storage capacity to be provided with allowance for the frequency of collection specified by the collection authority, the volume and nature of waste including recyclable material expected and the size and type of containers to be used

— responsibility for cleansing and maintenance of storage facilities

— environmental aspects, e.g. air pollution, indoor air quality, noise control, and litter abatement

— discharge of waste into sewers (e.g. food waste disposers)

— means of escape and firefighting arrangements in waste and recyclable material storage and collection areas

— appropriate arrangements for older persons and persons with disabilities.

For further guidance and information see:

— BS 5906: *Waste management in buildings. Code of practice*[64] (2005)

— CIBSE Guide G: *Public health engineering*[65] (chapter 4) (2004)

— Department for Environment, Food and Rural Affairs: *Introductory Guide: Options for the diversion of biodegradable municipal waste from landfill*[67] (2005)

— Biffaward/C-Tech Innovation Ltd: *Thermal methods of municipal waste treatment*[68] (2003)

## 3.10 Lifecycle impacts of materials and equipment

The abstraction, processing, transportation and disposal of materials and equipment is very energy intensive. Materials production and construction accounts for 30% of the total waste in the UK.

### 3.10.1 Principles

> The principles to apply relating to selection of sustainable materials and equipment are:
>
> — select materials and equipment from sustainable sources
>
> — select materials and equipment with the lowest in-use environmental impacts
>
> — select materials and equipment with the lowest embodied environmental impacts
>
> — select materials and equipment with high recycled content.
>
> Refer to the CIBSE online sustainable engineering tool[2] for practical measures and sources of guidance for each of these principles (www.cibse.org/sustain).

These principles would be applied by the project team. The building services engineer should work with the structural engineer and architect to ensure that the lifecycle impacts of materials and equipment are considered from the start of a project.

At the early stages in a project the following should be considered:

— whether refurbishment is a viable option to reduce the lifecycle impacts of a project

— assessment of the lifecycle impacts of materials and equipment that would affect the form and function of the building; e.g. ventilation strategy to reduce the need for plant and equipment, make appropriate use of thermal mass, and reduce the operational impact of the building

— opportunities to refurbish existing buildings or to use recycled or reclaimed materials.

More details on materials and equipment selection during the design stages of a project are set out in section 5.6 below.

### 3.10.2    Selecting materials and equipment

Materials and equipment should be selected based on their performance, durability and longevity as this will increase their lifecycle. Also consideration should be given to where the materials and equipment have been sourced and how far they have to be transported.

Embodied energy is often referred to when considering the lifecycle impacts of materials. Embodied energy is the amount of energy required to produce a product from extraction manufacture, transport, maintenance and disposal.

Both the BRE's *Green Guide to Specification*[5] and *Green Guide to Housing Specification*[6] suggest that embodied energy will become increasingly less useful as a measure of environmental impact as the amount of renewable energy that is used for manufacturing process increases.

The *Green Guides* propose an alternative to embodied energy by using parameters to reflect the environmental impacts resulting from the use of energy — fossil fuel depletion and pollutions caused by the creation of energy for a particular process (e.g. climate change, acid deposition, summer smog, toxicity etc.). The *Green Guides* rate construction systems and products based on their overall environmental impacts by using a life cycle assessment (LCA) approach.

For further information refer to:

— BRE: *Green Guide to Specification*[5] (2002)

— BRE *Green Guide to Housing Specification*[6] (2000).

For guidance specifically for building services, refer to:

— Barbour Index/ECD Energy & Environment Ltd: *Greening NES: A guide to sustainable engineering specification*[69] (2001).

### 3.10.2.1    *Construction methods*

The choice of construction method for a project can have a significant impact on the materials use of the project. Traditional methods of construction typically result in considerable wastage of materials and often do not involve recycling or reclamation of materials or components.

'Modern methods of construction' (MMC) is a collective term used to describe a number of new construction methods that are being introduced into the UK that differ significantly from so-called 'traditional' construction methods. These construction methods vary from volumetric (i.e. factory-produced three-dimension units stacked on site to form a building) to sub-assemblies and components (such as pre-fabricated floor and roof cassettes).

MMC have environmental benefits, particularly with regard to waste generated. Greater accuracy means that more components can be ordered cut to size, the construction process is sheltered from the weather, and there are storage facilities for materials. This all leads to less waste compared to site-based construction. Also, with manufactured systems it is possible to design with manufacture in mind, allowing dimensions to be 'tweaked' to fit standard material sizes.

Improvements in build quality for certain types of MMC should ensure consistent standards of insulation and service installation. There are disadvantages, such as the transportation impacts of moving the components from the factory to the site.

### 3.10.2.2    *Choice of materials and thermal mass*

Guidance on the appropriate use of thermal mass is set out in detail in various publications including CIBSE Guide A: *Environmental design*[70], CIBSE AM10: *Natural ventilation in non-domestic buildings*[19] and BRE Digest 454: *Thermal mass in office buildings*[71].

Based on the environmental profiles in the *Green Guide to Specification*[3], high thermal mass concrete is a poor performer in environmental terms.

For example, for upper floors, precast units can often substantially reduce the mass of the floor structure whilst maintaining high floor loadings and providing some thermal mass. Systems using hollow or lightweight components are likely to give the best environmental option. Table 14 is an extract from the *Green Guide to Specification*[3] and shows a comparison between different upper floor constructions.

Table 14 Environmental rating for various types of upper floors (source: BRE: *Green guide to Specification*[3])

| Upper floors | Summary rating |
| --- | --- |
| Beam and blockwork floor with screed | A |
| Hollow precast reinforced slab and screed | A |
| Hollow precast reinforced slab with structural topping | B |
| *In situ* reinforced concrete slab | C |
| *In situ* reinforced concrete trough slab | B |
| *In situ* reinforced concrete waffle slab | B |
| Lattice girder precast concrete floor with polystyrene void formers and *in situ* concrete topping | B |
| Profiled steel permanent steel shuttering, *in situ* concrete slab, steel reinforcement bars and mesh | B |
| Solid prestressed composite floor with structural topping | C |

### 3.11.1          Principles

> The principles to apply to the social impacts relating to developments are:
>
> — engage with the local community throughout the building lifecycle
>
> — maintain and enhance environmental quality
>
> — avoid nuisance pollution levels (including noise)
>
> — avoid causing other nuisances to neighbourhood building users.
>
> Refer to the CIBSE on-line sustainable engineering tool[2] for practical measures and sources of guidance for each of these principles (http://www.cibse.org/sustain).

These principles would be applied by the project team.

At the early stages of a project, the environmental quality is the key issue. Avoiding pollution and nuisance are considered as more detailed design issues, and are covered in section 5.7.

For all construction projects, it is important to consult with the local community and stakeholders. This process will help to address all of the above principles.

### 3.11.2          Community engagement

Engaging the local community in the development of designs and responding to their concerns demonstrates that a project is inclusive, transparent and responsive. Community or 'stakeholder' engagement is the recognised way of enabling and managing the involvements of parties that have an interest in a construction project. It means understanding and responding to ways in which the construction project affects, and is affected by stakeholders.

Stakeholder consultation is a compulsory part of the planning application process as planning documents are publicly available and people are given the opportunity to comment on the proposals. However, consultation is not limited to the planning stage. CIRIA document C627: *Engage: How to deliver socially responsible construction — a client's guide*[75] provides a comprehensive guide for construction professionals on how to address social issues associated with sustainable construction.

Table 16 gives examples of two-way engagement with stakeholders.

Some of the key priorities highlighted within CIRIA C627[75] are as follows:

— *Two-way engagement process*: consultation should be a two-way dialogue to ensure engagement as opposed to providing information. A positive example would be putting in place a process to capture complaints, assess number and cause and set up reduction target. Complainants should be kept informed of steps taken.

— *Responsiveness*: this is a key aspect of accountability. The value of engagement for stakeholders and client arises out of the changes made as a result of involvement in decision making. It does

**Table 16** Examples of two-way engagement compared to one-way engagement[75]

| One-way engagement | Two-way engagement |
|---|---|
| Informing the local residents of the likely noise impacts of a project | Putting into place a process to capture complaints, assess the number and cause of them, and set up meaningful reduction targets. Keeping complainants informed of steps taken. |
| Making a charitable donation to local community projects | Inviting representatives of local community projects and charities to a workshop to work out how they might be affected or could benefit from the construction project. |
| Informing local communities of the advantages to them of a new building in the area | Engaging the local community representatives to pool ideas about the scope of the project, encouraging innovation and meeting real needs. |
| Sourcing a local workforce | Setting up a job centre on site, to enable unemployed in local communities to find work in construction projects and elsewhere. |

not mean that views of stakeholders always are acted upon but reasons should be made clear for not acting.

For further information refer to:

— Neighbourhood Initiatives Foundation: *Planning for Real*[76] (http://www.communityplanning.net)

— CIRIA C627: *Engage: How to deliver socially responsible construction — a client's guide*[75] (2004)

### 3.11.3          Maintain and enhance environmental quality

At the early stages of a project, the key issue relating to environmental quality is the safety and security of the development.

#### 3.11.3.1          Safety and security

A safe environment is a fundamental issue to address if seeking a sustainable community. *Secured by Design*[77] and the *Park Mark — Safer Parking*[78] scheme are a police initiatives which aim to ensure the building industry adopts crime prevention measures in the design of developments. The *Secured by Design* initiative aims to reduce the opportunity for crime, reduce fear of crime, creating a safer and more secure environment.

Examples of some of the principles that require addressing as part of *Secured by Design* are as follows:

— Environmental quality and sense of ownership: avoiding opportunities for 'anonymity' of offenders, e.g. where public space directly abuts private space allowing offender in close proximity to private space without being noticed.

— Design lighting to reduce fear of crime: research shows that where public lighting is weak or patchy fear of crime is increased. Lighting combined with other community safety initiatives leads to reduced crime.

— In urban setting open spaces, footpaths and cycleway should be overlooked from buildings or traffic routes.

Addressing principles of *Secured by Design* has become a key consideration for landscape architects and architects alike. The key role for mechanical engineers is to ensure that consideration has been given to these principles by the wider design team and appropriate experts appointed where necessary. However, in some aspects building services engineers have specific role to ensure technology and measures are in place to support crime prevention measures in the development.

### 3.11.3.2    Key actions

The actions for building services engineers are as follows:

— highlight the need for consultation with local police architectural liaison officers

— discuss with design team whether a *Secured by Design* 'Developers Award' certificate is to be sought for residential developments

— assume direct responsibility to provide appropriate security lighting, taking into account appropriate energy efficiency measures

— assume direct responsibility to supply surveillance technology located in appropriate areas of the development and co-ordinated by a central control room where necessary

— work with architects to ensure internal core area and plant rooms address security.

For further information refer to:

— *Secured by Design*[77] (http://www.securedby design.com)

— *Park Mark — Safer Parking*[78] (http://www.secured carparks.com)

# 4    Supporting the planning application

This section sets out how building services engineers can provide essential advice to help projects receive planning approval.

'Sustainable development' is now the core principle underpinning planning, and providing advice on how projects can respond to planning policies is one of the key new business opportunities for building services engineers.

Regional and local planning polices are setting standards for sustainability. For example, the draft *Regional Spatial Strategy*[79] for the South West includes a policy (RE5) that states that:

Larger-scale developments will be expected to provide, as a minimum, sufficient on-site renewable energy to reduce $CO_2$ emissions from energy use by users of the buildings constructed on site by 10% ...

Building services engineers will be expected to be aware of relevant planning policies, particularly those related to $CO_2$ emissions, water use and other issues directly affected by building services design.

Most significant new build or refurbishment project will require a planning application to be submitted and therefore will have to respond to the relevant planning policies.

On larger projects a planning consultant will be appointed to manage the planning application. The planning consultant acts on behalf of the client and is responsible for interpreting planning policies, negotiating with the local authority planners on how the proposed development should respond to planning policies, and submitting the planning application. For smaller projects, it is often the architect who takes this role.

A summary of the planning process is shown in Figure 14[80]. It is important to note from this figure that:

— Outline applications can be made based on masterplans or early design proposals

— Detailed applications are typically made at *RIBA Plan of Work*[13] Stage C

— there can be a period of negotiation between local authority planners and the project team prior to the submission of the application to which the building services engineer may contribute

— the planning application may be changed or re-submitted for planning, which will involve additional work.

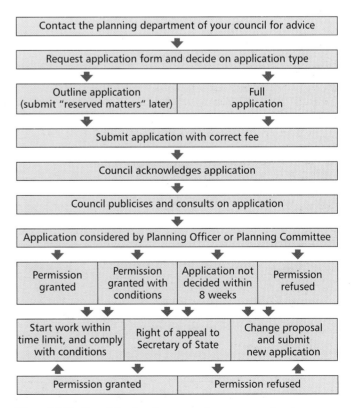

**Figure 14** Outline of the planning process (source: www.planning portal.gov.uk[80]; Crown copyright)

## 4.1      Planning policies

Planning applications are submitted to the local authority, which then determines whether planning permission is granted or refused. The local authority will have planning policies relating to sustainability and may set out specific requirements for sustainability statements (see 4.2.2 below) and/or may have a sustainability checklist to be completed. Many local authorities also have specific targets for low carbon buildings and for a percentage contribution from renewable energy.

CLG's draft Planning Policy Statement *Planning and Climate Change*[81] sets out how spatial planning should contribute to reducing emissions and stabilising climate change (mitigation) and take into account the unavoidable consequences (adaptation).

It will increase the pressure on new developments to:

—     meet low and zero carbon targets (see section 3.1)

—     take account of the effects of climate change (see section 3.3), and

—     provide a coherent response to issues related to climate change such as, flood risk, biodiversity and sustainable transport.

Table 17 summarises the national, regional and local planning hierarchy.

**Table 17** Summary of the national, regional and local planning policy hierarchy

| Level | Role |
|---|---|
| National | The Government determines national policies on different aspects of planning. National planning policies are set out in Planning Policy Statements (PPS) and Planning Policy Guidance notes (PPG). |
| Regional | In England (except London), regional planning bodies (in London, the Mayor of London) each prepare and produce a Regional Spatial Strategy (RSS) (in London, the Spatial Development Strategy) reflecting the needs and aspirations for development and land use for a ten to fifteen year period. |
| Local | Local planning authorities (other than county councils) must prepare a Local Development Framework (LDF). This will comprise a folder of documents for delivering the spatial or minerals planning strategy for the area. |

For a more complete list of planning policy documents and references, refer to Annex A in CIBSE's *Introduction to sustainability*[1].

## 4.2      Planning submission documents

Table 18 shows the key documents required for a major planning application.

### 4.2.1      Energy strategy reports

Energy strategy reports are currently required for major projects in London, that are referable to the Greater London Authority (GLA). However it is good practice to develop an energy statement in support of all major planning applications.

This report should demonstrate that the project design team has given thorough consideration to all zero and low $CO_2$ technologies that could be technically employed to meet a proportion of the building's energy demand.

The report should establish the building energy demand (based on energy modelling, rather than benchmarks) and show the energy and related $CO_2$ savings that can be made through energy efficiency measures, efficient supply of energy (such as combined heat and power) and incorporation of a variety of renewable energy sources. Finally the report should set out the project team's preferred energy strategy.

Sections 3.1 and 5.1 include information on the approach to developing an energy statement and more information can be found in the GLA's *Integrating renewable energy into new developments: Toolkit for planners, developers and consultants*[14].

### 4.2.2      Sustainability statements

Sustainability statements are becoming commonplace documents submitted in support of significant planning applications. There is not, however, any formal national guidance on what constitutes a sustainability statement when it is submitted in support of a planning application. Regional and local guidance is now provided. For examples, major projects in London now have to comply with the GLA's *Supplementary Planning Guidance on Sustainable Design and Construction*[15]. This guidance includes specific targets for a range of sustainability issues.

**Table 18** Planning submission documents

| Key document | Likely author | Comments |
|---|---|---|
| Environmental statement (ES) | Environmental consultants with a number of experts | See section 4.2.3 on environmental impact assessments and environmental statements. Information may be required from engineers on air quality from CHP etc. |
| Sustainability statement (SS) | Sustainability consultant | Often presented as a separate document, but can be included as an additional chapter in ES. Will draw on information from the energy strategy report. |
| Energy strategy report (currently mainly for projects in London) | Building services engineer | An energy strategy report should be prepared for major projects (see section 4.2.1). |
| Design and access statements | Architect | Should include sustainability issues relating to the architecture and accessibility of the scheme. |
| Planning statements | Planning consultant | Draws together and summarises the findings of all studies undertaken in support of planning to make the case for the granting of planning application for the site and seeks to demonstrate compliance with planning policy. |

### 4.2.3 Environmental impact assessments and environmental statements

Environmental impact assessment (EIA) is a systematic process that examines the predicted environmental consequences of development in construction and operation. EIA is documented as an environmental statement. An EIA is a statutory requirement under European Union Directives 85/337/EEC[82] and 97/11/EC[83] ('EIA Regulations') for certain public and private projects. The process involves a number of stages, as outlined in Figure 15.

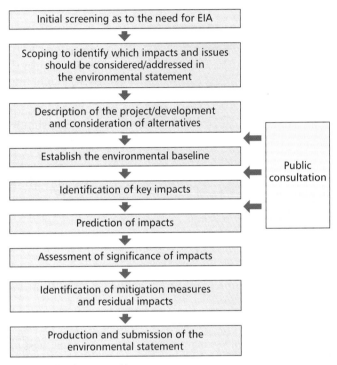

**Figure 15** Environmental impact assessment process

The first stage is screening, when a decision is made on whether the size and nature of the proposed development warrants an EIA. This can be done by requesting a 'screening opinion' from the local authority. Alternatively, a decision can be made by the project team. There are some projects that will always be screened for full assessment by virtue of their scale and potential environmental impacts (e.g. a new motorway or a crude-oil refinery).

A scoping opinion can then be requested from the planning authority to identify the environmental matters to be covered in the EIA.

For projects where an EIA is required, planning applicants will be expected to demonstrate to the local authority that the development proposals act to mitigate any environmental impacts to an acceptable level.

The EIA is documented as an environmental statement and in the case of planning applications is submitted by the developer to the local planning authority. The environmental statement should be an impartial but comprehensive and well organised set of documents. Most importantly, it must fulfil the requirements of the EIA Directive and associated legislation.

The checklist of potential issues that are covered by an EIA includes:

— soils and geology

— flora and fauna

— surface water (drainage, flood risk)

— groundwater

— contaminated land

— landscape

— visual aspects

— architectural heritage

— archaeology

— traffic, transport and access

— air quality

— noise and vibration

— microclimate (wind)

— daylight, sunlight and overshadowing

— socio-economic

— telecommunications

— sustainability.

## 4.3 Key actions

It is important to establish the strategy for the planning application by talking to the person co-ordinating the application. On larger projects a planning consultant will be appointed who is responsible for submitting the application.

The scope of work required to support the planning application needs to be determined before appointment. Therefore, the following has to be established well in advance of the application being submitted:

— the relevant local authority carbon or energy policies

— the relevant local authority sustainability policies, particularly those relating to energy, carbon and water policies, as these will be the direct responsibility of the building services engineer

— any relevant regional policies, as set out in the Regional Spatial Strategy

— specific requirements for the preparation of documents to accompany the planning application (e.g. energy strategy report, sustainability statement, environmental statement)

— whether an energy strategy report is required

— whether a sustainability statement and an environmental statement are required and what contribution is needed.

## 5 New design and refurbishment

This section sets out how building services engineers can influence the early stages of the building design and refurbishment process. It relates broadly to RIBA *Architect's Plan of Work*[13] Stages C and D.

Site-wide issues and strategic design decisions are addressed in section 3 above.

## 5.1 Energy efficient, low carbon design

### 5.1.1 Principles

> The principles for achieving energy efficient, low carbon buildings are:
>
> — reduce demand
>
> — meet end use demand efficiently
>
> — supply from low carbon sources
>
> — supply from renewable sources
>
> — enable energy management
>
> Refer to the CIBSE online sustainable engineering tool[2] for practical measures and sources of guidance for each of these principles (http://www.cibse.org/sustain).

These principles would be applied by the building services engineer.

### 5.1.2 Site opportunities and constraints

The first step is to undertake a review of site opportunities and constraints (e.g. ground conditions and contamination, wind resource, solar access, drainage capacity, existing buildings, space on site etc.). See section 3.1.3 for more information.

### 5.1.3 Understanding the building's energy profile

The next step is to develop predicted demand profiles for the building (challenge assumptions and benchmarks). Figure 16 shows peak monthly demands (kW) for heating and cooling.

It is important to note that CIBSE benchmarks are for design conditions to size plant and should not be used to predict energy demands. Instead, predicted energy demands should be generated from dynamic thermal modelling.

Modelling at early stages in the design process is becoming essential to ensure that proposals comply with Part L of the Building Regulations for England and Wales[17] and planning policies on energy.

CIBSE AM11: *Building energy and environmental modelling*[84] provides guidance for engineers on modelling and includes a software compliance checklist for appropriate models.

Outputs from the simulation program would normally include hourly demands (in kW) for heating (both mechanical ventilation and perimeter room heating), cooling (mechanical ventilation) and electricity (including small power, lighting and electrical consumption from mechanical ventilation systems). An allowance for domestic hot water (DHW) energy requirements should also be made.

The impacts of climate change on increased cooling demand should be considered, see section 3.3 and CIBSE TM36: *Climate change and the indoor environment*[35].

### 5.1.4 Reduce demand

The project team should consider:

— the available daylight to reduce electric lighting requirement

— avoiding overheating from solar gains

— where appropriate, utilise exposed thermal mass as part of a night-cooling strategy.

In England and Wales*, insulation standards must achieve the minimum area-weighted *U*-values as set out in Building Regulations Approved Document L[17]. Thermal modelling should assess whether there is any advantage from improving on these standards. Building Regulations Part L should be considered as a minimum standard and not an aspirational target.

The building envelope should be designed to eliminate thermal bridging (heat loss through conduction directly to the environment) and promote the continuity of insulation, thus minimising building fabric losses.

It is important to reduce the peak demands for energy as well as reducing annual energy demands to reduce the size of plant and equipment.

Approved Document L[17] also requires all new buildings to be pressure tested. Paragraph 39 of the Approved Document states that a reasonable limit for the design air permeability is 10 m³/(h·m²) at 50 Pa. For the majority of the year air leakage could be considered as energy leakage, the air in the building having been heated or cooled to provide thermal comfort. Buildings should be designed to achieve air permeability rates that are significantly lower than minimum standards set by Approved Document L. For more information, see CIBSE TM23: *Testing buildings for air leakage*[85].

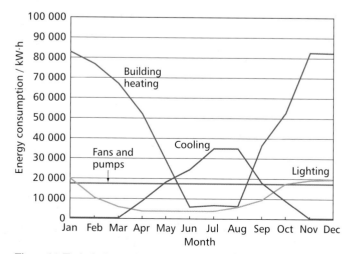

**Figure 16** Typical 12-monthly heating and cooling demand profile

---

* Similar legislation applies in Scotland and Northern Ireland

For larger buildings a building management system (BMS) should be installed to monitor all end uses separately to assist the building manager in monitoring and tuning the performance of the M&E systems to operate at higher efficiencies. This should be formatted to capture and present information on an hourly, daily, weekly, monthly or annual basis, such that any unreasonably high energy consumption trends can be readily identified, investigated and remedied.

More information on reducing demand can be found in a range of publications including CIBSE Guide F[16] and CIBSE AM10[19].

For specific measures on reducing energy demand and further references see the CIBSE online sustainable engineering tool[2] (http://www.cibse.org/sustain).

### 5.1.5 Meet demand efficiently

Once the energy demand has been reduced as far as possible, various energy efficient technologies can be applied to meet the remaining energy demand for a building. Technologies to meet the demand efficiently include a wide range of energy efficient technologies such as variable speed drives, low-energy lighting and efficient boilers. These technologies are covered in detail in CIBSE Guide F: *Energy efficiency in buildings*[16] and therefore have not been addressed in the present Guide.

Low and zero carbon technologies should be investigated before the feasibility of renewable energy is considered.

Table 19 sets out the low carbon technologies that can be applied to individual buildings.

**Table 19** Low carbon options for individual buildings

| Individual dwellings | Individual non-domestic buildings |
| --- | --- |
| Gas-fired micro-CHP | Gas-fired CHP and tri-generation (gas-fired CHP + absorption cooling) |
| Fuel cells (in early stages of development) | Fuel cells (in early stages of development) |

#### 5.1.5.1 Gas-fired CHP and tri-generation

Combined heat and power (CHP) is a process involving simultaneous generation of heat and electricity, where the heat generated in the process is harnessed via heat recovery equipment for heating and/or cooling. Conventional electricity generation is typically 35% efficient, with the most advanced technologies achieving up to 55%. The remaining 45–65% is lost as waste heat. CHP plants can achieve overall fuel efficiencies of up to 90% by generating electricity and recovering heat. In buildings, the recovered heat can be used for space heating and domestic hot water (DHW).

CHP only saves carbon dioxide and money when it is operating; rules of thumb suggest that a system should be running for a minimum of 4500 hours per year for it to be financially viable.

CHP systems can use various types of plant and fuel including gas turbines, steam turbines, internal combustion engines and fuel cells. The most common fuel used is natural gas, favoured for being clean and enabling a high degree of controllability. Other fuels include diesel, biodiesel, landfill gas, biomass, municipal waste, etc. System efficiencies depend on the type of plant and fuel used. The ratio of electricity to heat output from CHP also varies with the type of plant, ranging from a 1:1 ratio for diesel engines to as much as 1:3 for some gas-fired plant.

CHP is typically sized to meet the base heat load and so the interaction with on-site renewable energy technologies has to be considered.

Detailed information on CHP is set out in CIBSE Guide AM12: *Small-scale combined heat and power for buildings*[86] and Good Practice Guide GPG043[87]. The following organisations also provide extensive guidance on the feasibility and design of gas-fired CHP systems:

— The Carbon Trust (http://www.carbontrust.co.uk)

— Combined Heat and Power Association (http://www.chpa.co.uk).

Tri-generation provides cooling as well as heating and electricity. The cooling is provided by absorption chillers that use heat from the CHP plant to produce a cooling effect. In most cases, absorption cooling is chosen as a less environmentally damaging alternative to other technologies, by making use of heat that would otherwise be wasted.

For more information on absorption cooling, refer to Good Practice Guide GPG256: *An introduction to absorbtion cooling*[88].

#### 5.1.5.2 Fuel cells

Fuel cells convert chemical energy directly into electricity by combining hydrogen and oxygen in a controlled reaction. They emit virtually no pollution as the products of this reaction are electricity, heat and water vapour. If the waste heat is used, up to 80% fuel efficiency can be achieved.

Fuel cell-based CHP systems have an edge in terms of cleanliness, reliability and maintenance over conventional CHP systems, but their main advantage is often seen as their particularly high electrical efficiency. This is far superior to conventional and other newer CHP and micro-CHP technologies. Fuel cells are also very quiet compared with conventional CHP.

Fuel cells are very expensive compared with other low and zero carbon technologies. Grants are available to encourage use of fuel cells, though these are only likely to amount to around 50% of total capital cost so even with this the technology would not compete with conventional CHP on cost.

Fuel cells are commercially available but systems are generally at early stages of commercialisation and so projects have substantial technology risk. At present operation and maintenance costs are high; however costs are declining rapidly.

## 5.1.6        Renewable energy technologies

Table 20 sets out the renewable technologies that can be applied to individual buildings.

**Table 20**  Renewable technology options for individual buildings

| Individual dwellings | Individual non-domestic buildings |
| --- | --- |
| Solar water heating and solar air collectors | Solar hot water heating for buildings with significant hot water load |
| Building mounted micro-wind turbines | Building mounted wind turbines |
| Photovoltaic panels or slates | Building integrated photovoltaics; e.g. cladding, louvre shading, and glazing |
| Biomass boilers or stoves | Biomass boilers with absorption cooling |
| Ground source heat pumps (considered a 'renewable' technology in the GLA renewables toolkit[14]) | Ground source heating and cooling (considered a 'renewable' technology in the GLA renewables toolkit[14]) |

### 5.1.6.1       Solar water heating

Solar water heating systems use the energy from the sun to heat water, most commonly in the UK for hot water needs. The systems use a heat collector, generally mounted on the roof or a south facing façade in which a fluid is heated by the sun. This fluid is used to heat water that is stored in either a separate hot water cylinder or more commonly a twin coil hot water cylinder with the second coil providing top-up heating from a conventional boiler. Ideally the collectors should be mounted in a south-facing location, although south-east/south-west orientatations within 45° of south will also function successfully. The panels can be bolted onto the roof or walls or integrated into the roof.

There are two standard types of collectors used: flat plate and evacuated tube. The flat plate collector, see Figure 17, is the predominant type used in solar domestic hot water systems, as they tend to have a lower cost for each unit of energy saved. Evacuated tube collectors, see Figure 18, are

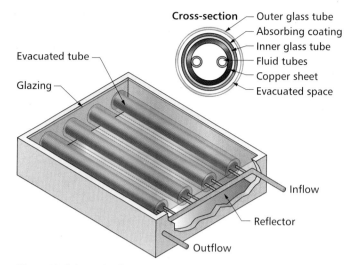

**Figure 18**  Schematic of an evacuated tube solar water heating panel

generally more expensive due to the complex manufacturing process required to achieve the vacuum, but manufacturers generally claim better winter all-round performance.

### 5.1.6.2       Solar air collectors

Air-based solar collectors use air as the heat transfer medium instead of liquid, see Figure 19. These systems normally use an absorber plate (a sheet of heat-absorbing material) to collect the heat and then transfer it to the air flowing over the plate.

Absorber plates can be used in a variety of ways:

— in open or closed systems

— with single or double-pass air flow

— fan-driven or operating through natural convection

— as part of an identifiable connector or integrated into the fabric of the building.

Closed systems use one or two panes of glass through which the sun's rays pass before hitting the absorber plate.

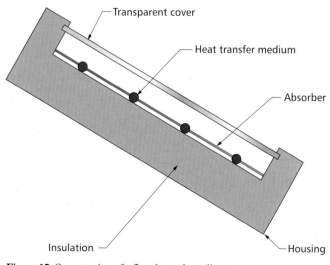

**Figure 17**  Cross section of a flat plate solar collector

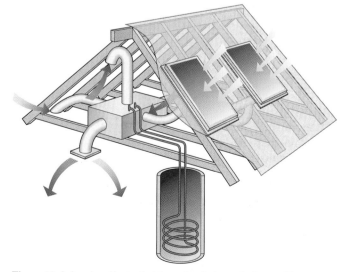

**Figure 19**  Solar air collector (with mechanical ventilation and heat recovery)

Applications for solar air heating systems include building ventilation air heating and process air heating. Systems used for ventilation heating vary depending on whether the building is for industrial, commercial or residential use.

### 5.1.6.3 Photovoltaics

Photovoltaic (PV) systems convert energy from the sun into electricity through semi conductor cells. Systems consist of semiconductor cells connected together and mounted into modules. Modules are connected to an inverter to convert their direct current (DC) in to alternating current (AC), which is usable in buildings. PV can supply electricity either to the buildings to which they are attached, or when the building demand is insufficient, electricity can be exported to the electricity grid.

For PV to work effectively it should ideally face south and at an incline of 30° to the horizontal, although orientations within 45° of south are acceptable and will function successfully. It is essential that the system is unshaded, as even a small shadow may significantly reduce output. Figure 20 shows how PV efficiency varies depending on panel orientation and pitch.

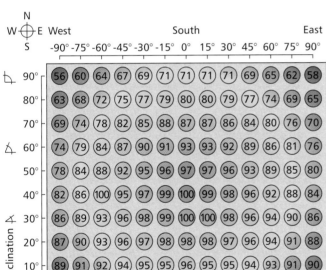

**Figure 20** Photovoltaic energy yield relative to inclination and orientation (reproduced by permission of solarcentury.com)

PVs are available in a number of forms including monocrystalline, polycrystalline, amorphous silicon (thin film) or hybrid panels that are mounted on or integrated into the roof or facades of buildings. Examples of building integrated photovoltaic products that can be incorporated into buildings include:

— rainscreen cladding intregrated into the façade

— shading louvres with integrated photovoltaics

— photovoltaics integrated into glazing

— panels bolted on to the roof

— tilted panels on a flat roof

— thin film laid on a standing seam roof

— solar tiles.

PV system size is measured in kWp. A 1 kWp polycrystalline system will generate around 750 kW·h of electricity a year in the south of England. The size of the PV systems can be varied to match the carbon saving required.

### 5.1.6.4 Biomass-fired heating

The Biomass Energy Centre (http://www.biomassenergy centre.org.uk) defines biomass as 'material that is derived from living, or recently living biological organisms' and includes virgin wood, expressly cultivated energy crops, agricultural residues, food waste and specific types of industrial waste and co-products.

Biofuel is 'solid, liquid or gaseous fuel that is derived from biomass … that has been processed or converted in some way into a more convenient form, principally to increase energy density.'

The main biofuel for heating and CHP is wood chip and pellets. A number of CHP manufacturers produce engines that run on biodiesel or pellets, and biogas (produced by gasification of solid biomass) has been used as a fuel. There are also engines that can run on more than one type of fuel.

For any biomass application, the biofuel supply in the local area has to be investigated, both in terms of the raw biomass resource and the existing or potential capacity to produce a usable fuel.

Biomass heating simply involves burning a biofuel rather than a fossil fuel (typically gas or oil) in a boiler. As with fossil fuels, the boiler must be designed to suit the fuel to be used. Like oil, fuel must be delivered to site and stored in sufficient quantity to meet demand for a reasonable period.

Biomass in the form of wood chips and pellets is often considered a carbon neutral fuel, as the carbon dioxide emitted during burning has been (relatively) recently absorbed from the atmosphere by photosynthesis and no fossil fuel is involved. However, biomass is assigned a carbon emission factor of 0.025 $kgCO_2$/kW·h to account for the carbon emissions associated with transport and processing (see section 3.1.7.4). The wood is normally seen as a by-product of other industries. Biomass from coppicing is likely to have some external energy inputs, for fertiliser, cutting, drying etc. and these may need to be considered in the future.

Wood from forests, urban tree pruning, farmed coppices or farm and factory waste can be burnt directly to provide heat in buildings, although nowadays most of these wood sources are commercially available in the form of wood chips or pellets, which makes transport and handling on site easier.

Fully automated biomass boiler technology is well developed and established. A biomass boiler system would typically include a fully automated auger fed boiler plant, fuel hopper and buffer vessel to balance the load on the boiler and help meet peak demands.

Table 21 compares the energy density of biomass fuels.

**Table 21** Characteristics of biomass fuels (source: based on information from the Biomass Energy Centre)

| Fuel | Energy density by mass / (kW·h/tonne) | Bulk density / (tonnes/m³) | Energy density by volume / (kW·h/m³) |
|---|---|---|---|
| Wood chips*: | 2000–4000 | 0.175–0.35 | 600–1000 |
| — 22% m.c.† | 3700 | | |
| — 30% m.c.† | 3500 | | |
| — 50% m.c.† | 3200 | | |
| — 40% m.c.† | 2800 | | |
| Log wood (stacked, air dry: 20% m.c.) | 4200 | 0.3–0.55 | 1300–2300 |
| Wood (solid, oven dry) | 5000–5800 | 0.45–0.8 | 2300–4600 |
| Wood pellets | 5000 | 0.6–0.7 | 3000–3500 |
| Miscanthus (bale) | 4700 | 0.12–0.16 | 560–750 |
| Coal (lignite to anthracite) | 5600–8300 | 0.8–1.1 | 4500–9100 |
| Oil | 11 700 | 0.87 | 10 200 |
| Natural gas (NTP) | 15 000 | 0.0007 | 10.8 |

\* Very dependent on moisture content (m.c.)

† Wood energy

*Note*: m.c. = moisture content

### 5.1.6.5    Small scale biomass-fired CHP

Biomass CHP systems using gasification of biomass have been tested for possible application in housing schemes and provide a theoretically attractive solution to meeting heating and electrical demands with renewables. Biomass gasification CHP is the type of system trialled by the Peabody Trust at the Beddington Zero Energy Development ('BedZED') scheme in Sutton[89]. An alternative system currently in development is based on an externally-fired gas turbine.

These technologies may become viable in the future as companies overcome technical barriers and develop successful technology at this scale.

### 5.1.6.6    Wind turbines

The wind resource in the UK is a major renewable source for power overall. However, this is not universally true across the country. Exposed and coastal sites in the west, east and north have appropriate wind regimes as do off-shore sites currently being developed as part of the national renewable power initiative.

It should be noted that the electricity generated at any one time by a wind turbine is highly dependent on the speed of the wind at the site of the turbine. The wind speed itself is dependent on factors such as the location within the UK, nearby obstructions such as buildings and trees, and the height of the turbine above ground level. Ideally, a professional assessment of the local wind speed should be undertaken for a full year at the exact location where the turbine is to be installed. In practice, this may be difficult, expensive and time consuming to undertake so an assessment based on the average wind speed and the nearby obstacles will have to be used.

Wind energy installations can range from small domestic turbines to large commercial developments. At the smaller end of the scale, turbines of 1 to 2.5 kW can be mounted on buildings and whilst there are currently few practical implementations of building mounted wind turbines in the UK several manufacturers are preparing to mass produce smaller scale building mounted turbines. It should be noted that this is an emerging market and there are emerging performance and safety standards. It is likely to be more difficult to find suitable sites for small building-mounted wind turbines in urban areas due to the disturbed air.

The British Wind Energy Association (http://www.bwea.com) notes that an average speed of 7 m/s is needed for viable systems and that, in general, most small/micro wind turbines start to generate electricity in wind speeds of approximately 3–4 m/s, and most products achieve their maximum, or rated output at a wind speed of 10–12 m/s[90]. This should be considered when comparing products.

Small scale micro-turbines have a diameter of around two metres and require mounting on a pole which increases the turbine overall height. Typically these turbines are mounted above roof level, as the increased height usually means greater wind speeds.

Wind turbines on buildings are usually very visible and can have implications on planning especially in conservation areas. Installation of building mounted wind turbines should be discussed with the local authority planning department.

At a community level, wind turbines can be used to generate the energy requirements of a community building or group of buildings, perhaps selling any surplus energy to the grid. On a commercial scale, remote wind turbines measuring up to 140 m tall with capacities of over 2 MW each are used to generate electricity sold directly into the electricity grid.

Indicative characteristics for a range of sizes of wind turbine are shown in Table 22. The largest turbine is akin to those used in medium scale wind farms and industrial 'merchant wind' applications. Turbines at the upper end of this size range are likely to be inappropriate in a residential environment due to issues such as noise, shadow flicker (see below), and visual impact on all but the largest sites.

Noise levels generated from wind turbines should be assessed in relation to existing and predicted background noise levels for the specific site. The assessment will include both day and night assessments and acceptable limits vary for different building uses. Despite the maturity of the wind industry there is no official guidance on the separation to be maintained between turbines and surrounding development in terms of either minimum distances or areas.

Developers may refer to DTI report ETSU-R-97: *Assessment and rating of noise from wind farms*[91] when assessing a site for planning purposes.

Shadow flicker is caused by sunlight shining onto a building from behind a wind turbine at a particular time of day and year and is very site specific. The shadow of the blades rotating will cause a flickering effect which can be

**Table 22** Indicative characteristics for a range of wind turbines

| Item | Wind turbine rating | | | | | | |
|---|---|---|---|---|---|---|---|
| | 0.6–1.0 kW | 1.2–3.0 kW | 5.0–6.0 kW | 15–25 kW | 50–18 kW | 150–250 kW | 0.6–2.0 MW |
| Rated windspeed (m/s) | 10–17 | 10–16 | 10–17 | 11–14 | 11–12 | 12 | 12–16 |
| Cut-in windspeed (m/s) | 2.5–3.5 | 2.5–3.5 | 2.5–4 | 2.6-4 | 2.5-4.6 | 3 | 2.5-3.5 |
| Turbine diameter (m) | 1.7–2.7 | 2–5 | 3.1–6 | 10–11 | 15–18 | 26–32 | 44–82 |
| Hub height (m) | 5–18 | 6.5–18 | 9–24 | 13–32 | 25–41 | >36 | 55–138 |
| Manufacturer's quoted annual energy (electricity) generation (kW·h/year) | 900–1896 | 2500–9534 | 5000–12 000 | 60 000 | 155 000–225 000 | 656 000 | 1.9–4.0 million |
| Average wind speed corresponding to quoted annual energy generation (m/s) | 5–6 | 5–6 | 5–5.8 | 6.5 | 7 | 7 | N/A |

*Note*: This table is based on a sample of products on the DTI's Low Carbon Buildings Programme list of systems eligible for grant funding at the time of publication, except for the 0.6–2 MW rated turbines. The current list of manufacturers with eligible products is available from the Low Carbon Buildings programme website (http://www.lowcarbonbuildings.org.uk).

both a nuisance and a potential hazard to residents when viewed through a narrow opening. Such flickering should not be visible at distances of approximately 10 rotor diameters. However, buildings located to the north of a turbine site may be affected. Shadow flicker can be a particular issue for residential buildings. Other than siting turbines to avoid the effect, the only mitigation available is to shut the turbine down at the specific periods of the year when shadow flicker is an issue.

### 5.1.6.7 Ground source heating and cooling

Ground source heating and cooling is used here as a 'catch-all' for a group of technologies that use the relatively stable low temperature (compared to the indoor setpoint) of the ground or bodies of water as a source for providing heating and cooling in buildings. The transfer of heat between the ground/water and the indoor space can be direct (heat is transferred directly from the ground/water to the space) or indirect (a heat transfer medium transfers heat from the ground/water to the space), with a theoretical range of system types as shown in Table 23.

Of the system types shown in the table, indirect systems are more widely replicable. While indirect water-sourced heating/cooling may be applicable where an appropriate body of water is available, ground source heating/cooling is the most common of these technologies. Ground source heating and cooling is achieved using ground source heat pumps.

It should be noted that ground water temperatures are not guaranteed and appropriate tests should be undertaken as early as possible.

Heat pumps use the refrigeration cycle to transfer heat between a relatively cold source and a relatively hot sink. Heat pumps can be used to provide either cooling or heating. The capability of systems to operate in heating and/or cooling modes depends on their design in response to the needs of the buildings. Reversible heat pumps deliver both cooling and heating and are common as 'split' systems where in heating mode they are operating as air source heat pumps.

A ground source heat pump (GSHP) uses the ground (via a ground coil) as the source of heat, with the building water circuit (the heating circuit in this mode) as the sink. In reversible systems, in cooling mode the building water circuit is the cooling circuit and heat source, and the ground is the heat sink.

The attraction of the ground as a heat source for GSHPs is based on the assumption that beyond a certain depth (around 10 m), ground temperatures stay effectively constant at approximately the annual average air temperature — between 10 °C and 14 °C in the UK (e.g. ~12 °C in London). Heat pump performance is better when the difference between source and sink temperatures is lower. The seasonal performance of ground source heat pumps will be better than for an air source heat pump because air temperatures will often be below 12 °C over the course of the heating season.

There is some debate about the status of heat pumps as a renewable technology because they use grid electricity. However, the GLA renewables toolkit[14] includes GSHPs as a renewable technology. There is no conceptual difference between the use of electricity to power a pump in a solar water heating system and a compressor in a heat pump. A

**Table 23** Theoretical range of ground source heating and cooling systems

| Source | Examples of direct systems | Examples of indirect systems | |
|---|---|---|---|
| | | Open loop | Closed loop |
| Ground | Earth sheltering | Pre-cooling of ventilation air using ground heat exchange pipes | Closed loop ground source heat pump |
| Water | Open loop systems with water abstracted from a lake, river or ground water aquifer circulated in a 'chilled' water circuit | Open loop systems with heat exchange between abstracted water and building chilled water circuit | Closed loop systems with heat exchange coil located in a lake or river |

solar water heating system can be made '100% renewable' by using a PV powered pump, and the same principle applies to heat pumps. The practical difference is in the quantity of energy transfer from the renewable source relative to the quantity of electricity required to operate the system.

For heat pumps the ratio of useful output to energy input is:

— *heating mode*: coefficient of performance (COP)

— *cooling mode*: energy efficiency ratio (EER)

The COP and EER of a system vary during system operation and are quoted as seasonal averages (analogous to the seasonal efficiency of boilers). The Building Regulations *Non-domestic heating, cooling and ventilation compliance guide*[92] sets a minimum COP for heat pumps of 2.0 when operating at design conditions and a minimum seasonal EER (SEER) for comfort cooling with a water loop heat pump of 3.2. Examples of GSHPs can be found with COPs above 4.5 and SEERs of 5.5 quoted by manufacturers.

While heat pumps are regarded as 'renewable' in principle, a more general concern is whether they reduce carbon emissions relative to alternative options for heating and, if so, by how much. Gas (the most common alternative heating fuel) has lower $CO_2$ emissions per kW·h delivered than electricity. GSHPs used for heating can reduce $CO_2$ emissions as long as the seasonal COP is higher than the ratio of electricity to gas $CO_2$ emissions factors. Using the emissions factors given in Building Regulations Approved Document L[17] of 0.422 $kgCO_2$/kW·h for electricity and 0.194 $kgCO_2$/kW·h for gas gives a ratio of 2.18. So a heat pump with a seasonal COP greater than 2.18 replacing a gas boiler can reduce $CO_2$ emissions from building energy use.

Typical ground source heat pump systems will use a ground coil installed in a vertical borehole, or horizontally up to a few metres below the finished ground level. With

**Figure 21** Ground source heating pile during installation

piled foundations it is also possible to integrate the ground loop in the piling system. With these 'energy piles', see Figure 21, the pipework for the ground coil is attached to the reinforcing cages at the factory or on site and cast into the concrete.

### 5.1.7    Key actions

Building services engineers should design a low/zero carbon building by:

— identifying the options for reducing demand, supplying efficiently and for providing low or zero carbon technologies

— proposing feasible technologies and techniques to meet carbon emissions targets.

## 5.2    Water efficient design

### 5.2.1    Principles

---
The principles for water efficient design are:

— reduce demand (and waste)

— meet demand efficiently

— supply collected rainwater or recycled grey water

— recycle black water close to the point of use, if appropriate

— enable water management

Refer to the CIBSE online sustainable engineering tool[2] for practical measures and sources of guidance for each of these principles (http://www.cibse.org/sustain).

---

These principles would be applied by the building services engineers.

### 5.2.2    Review of infrastructure capacity

The infrastructure capacity may already have been established for the site (see section 3.2.2 above). If not, then this information should be requested from the statutory authorities for both the mains water supply and waste water leaving the site. This request will need to establish whether there are any capacity restrictions or discharge restrictions that would effect the development of the site.

The Environment Agency (http://www.environment-agency.gov.uk) and British Geological Survey (http://www.bgs.ac.uk) should be contacted to determine the location of existing boreholes and to discuss potential new boreholes and abstraction licences. This work would typically be undertaken in conjunction with the hydrologist or civil engineers for the project.

### 5.2.3    Predict demand for the building

It is unlikely that specific water consumption data will be available, in which case water demand is estimated from a knowledge of the likely use of the building, assisted by typical water consumption data such as those given in section 2 of CIBSE Guide G: *Public health engineering*[65].

However, it should be remembered that CIBSE consumption figures are maximum figures intended for peak design purposes (i.e. a worst case scenario) and they do not allow for water efficient fixtures and fittings that should considerably reduce the demand. It may be more realistic to apply a usage factor of 60–70% to these figures in recognition that not all of the possible consumption will actually take place[93].

Reducing the demand will reduce the capacity of the systems required for supplying, pumping, storing, treating and disposing of water.

Improving water demand estimates also relates to the sizing and efficiency of solar hot water heating systems.

The Environment Agency provides typical and best practice benchmarks for a range of building types (taken from the Watermark Project for the government estate[94]; http://www.watermark.gov.uk). An example of the data is provided in Table 23.

Targets for water use in dwellings are set out in the *Code for Sustainable Homes*[4] and are shown in Table 24.

Sources of water benchmark data include the following:

— CIRIA W10: *Key performance indicators for water use in hotels*[95] (2006)

— CIRIA W11: *Key performance indicators for water use in offices*[96] (2006)

Communities and Local Government: *Code for Sustainable Homes — a step change in sustainable home building practice*[4] (2006)

— Envirowise (http://www.envirowise.gov.uk) provides a simple benchmarking tool for a limited number of industries in terms of $m^3/m^3$ of product, $m^3$/tonne of product and $m^3$/employee.

— The water companies' websites often provide historical data.

Table 24 Water use benchmarks for dwellings (source: *Code for Sustainable Homes*[4])

| Standard | Code level | Internal potable water consumption / (litres/person) per day |
|---|---|---|
| Minimum | 1 and 2 | 120 |
| Good practice | 3 and 4 | 105 |
| Exemplar | 5 and 6 | 80 |

### 5.2.4    Reduce demand

The principle of reducing water demand refers to avoiding the need to use water, before looking at efficiency. Considering the major and obvious uses of water in buildings (flushing wastes, washing, cleaning, irrigation, and drinking) the scope for reducing demand is limited. Opportunities include:

— avoiding indoor and outdoor planting with high irrigation needs, e.g. by preferring drought-tolerant plant varieties

— preferring non-water-based heat rejection plant (bearing in mind the trade-off with energy use)

— avoiding water features that have no indispensable amenity value.

Detecting leakage and waste on the building side of the main water meter can be considered to reduce demand. Examples suitable for commercial buildings include:

— check meters to help to breakdown water use (e.g. different tenancy areas) and identify areas of high water use

— leak detection that monitors the mains water demand profile and raises an alarm on the building management system if there is a radical change in the demand profile (see BREEAM[97] for more information)

Table 23 Water use benchmarks for non-domestic buildings (source: the Watermark Project[94])

| Building | Typical | Best practice | Units | Number of buildings in survey |
|---|---|---|---|---|
| Offices | 9.3 | 6.4 | $m^3$/person per year | 500 |
| Schools | | | | 14 330 |
| — primary with pool | 4.3 | 3.1 | $m^3$/pupil per year | |
| — primary without pool | 3.8 | 2.7 | $m^3$/pupil per year | |
| — secondary with pool | 5.1 | 3.6 | $m^3$/pupil per year | |
| — secondary without pool | 3.9 | 2.7 | $m^3$/pupil per year | |
| Hospitals | | | | 273 |
| — large acute or teaching | 1.66 | 1.38 | $m^3/m^2$ floor area per year | |
| — small acute or long stay without personal laundry | 1.17 | 0.90 | $m^3/m^2$ floor area per year | |
| — small acute or long stay with personal laundry | 1.56 | 1.24 | $m^3/m^2$ floor area per year | |
| Museums and art galleries | 0.332 | 0.181 | $m^3/m^2$ floor area per year | 50 |
| Nursing homes | 80.6 | 68.5 | $m^3$/resident per year | 70 |
| Colleges and universities | 0.62 | 0.40 | $m^3/m^2$ floor area per year | 127 |
| Sports centres | 0.0385 | 0.0305 | $m^3$/visitor per year | 65 |
| Libraries | 0.203 | 0.128 | $m^3/m^2$ floor area per year | 89 |
| Community centres | 0.326 | 0.173 | $m^3/m^2$ floor area per year | 62 |

— sanitary supply shut off, which automatically turns off the water supply to a washroom that has been vacant for a period of time; this is particularly useful to avoid waste from dripping taps or faulty connections when the building is not occupied (see BREEAM[97] for more information).

## 5.2.5 Water efficiency

The principle of water efficiency is to reduce the quantity of water needed to satisfy any particular end use demand.

Examples of efficiency measures would be:

— dual, low flush WCs

— urinal flushing controls

— spray/aerating taps

— water efficient appliances

— low flow showers

— waterless urinals

— composting toilets.

Water use for commissioning, operation and maintenance of building services plant (e.g. cold water pipework and storage, cooling towers, irrigation, fire sprinkler systems, etc.) should also be considered.

## 5.2.6 Recycled/reclaimed water

Reclaiming and recycling waste water on site can help reduce demand for potable mains water and reduce pumping distances (and associated carbon emissions). There are three main sources of waste water: rainwater, grey water and black water. See section 3.2.5 for definitions of the different types of reclaimed and recycled water. The potential for using groundwater as a source of water should also be considered.

### 5.2.6.1    Rainwater collection

Rainwater from roofs and hard surfaces such as car parks can be stored and reused ('harvested'). The collected water can be used for non-potable purposes, such as watering gardens or flushing toilets. Rainwater may not require disinfection or physical/biological treatment to allow it to be stored and reused for some purposes.

A rainwater storage tank (or tanks) (preferably underground, which helps to maintain low storage temperatures, prevent light penetration and hence possible algae growth) with filtration units (particle filtration and possibly UV disinfection) and boosting sets will be required, see Figure 22. A back-up mains water supply should also serve the tank to provide a top-up supply during drought periods. The use of a separate pipework system will be required to ensure that potable supplies do not become contaminated.

Water demand rarely coincides with the supply of rainfall and storage is essential to ensure the system works satisfactorily with the maximum demand achieved from rainwater. The storage tanks should be sized to meet as much of the demand from rainwater as possible.

Inclusion of rainwater collection would provide water storage capacity and mean that the cold water storage capacities within the building, as set out in CIBSE Guide G[65], can be reduced.

In order to ensure maximum efficiency (and hence use as little mains water as possible) the annual yield of reclaimed water should, as near as possible, match the estimated annual demand.

Rainwater can generally be stored for 10–20 days[93] depending on the amount of contaminants in the water. This is helpful to ensure sufficient collection of water during wet periods to cover for drier periods. For the UK, estimated efficiencies of up to 90% are feasible with 10 days' storage, rising close to 100% with 20 days' storage.

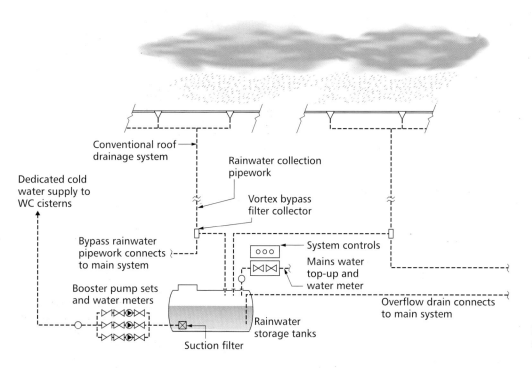

**Figure 22** Schematic of a rainwater collection system

Guidance on rainwater and grey water is available in:

— CIBSE KS01: *Reclaimed water*[93] (2005)

For further guidance see:

— CIRIA C539: *Rainwater and grey water use in buildings*[98] (2001)

— CIRIA Project Report PR 80: *Rainwater and grey water use in buildings: decision-making for water conservation*[99] (2001)

— BSRIA TN6/02: *Water reclamation guidance — design and construction of systems using grey water*[100] (2002)

— CIBSE Guide G: *Public health engineering*[65] (2004)

— Institute of Plumbing and Heating Engineering: *Plumbing engineering services design guide*[101] (2002)

Also, reference can be made to the UK Rainwater Harvesting Association (http://www.ukrha.org).

### 5.2.6.2 Grey water systems

For grey water systems, storage capacity should be kept as small as possible to ensure a fast turnaround of the water so that there is less time for bacteria to multiply. The appropriate storage duration is dependent on the source of the water and any treatment methods applied to the water.

There are communal and individual grey water systems available. Both systems require management to maintain filters and water quality.

Figure 23 shows an example of a communal system that uses a deep bed filtration system. The system uses grey water supplied from showers, baths and sinks (not the kitchen) and approximately matches the WC flushing demand. There is a high level of water cleaning which enables a longer storage time. The system is only suitable for high density areas.

There are individual systems available that can be applied to one or two WCs. These are simple systems with low levels of treatment and they are designed to require little maintenance. The system automatically flushes through with mains water, if the WC has not been used for a couple of days in order to avoid stagnation.

### 5.2.6.3 Black water treatment

Sewage effluent, or black water, can be treated on site to produce sludge and water. The water can either be recycled for non-potable uses or discharged into a local watercourse.

Whether treatment is on site or not, systems usually comprise three stages[102]:

— *Primary treatment*: a physical process which usually involves slowing down the sewage to allow gross solid matter to settle out.

— *Secondary treatment*: this removes most of soluble organic content and thus removes most of the BOD (biochemical oxygen demand) through oxygenation.

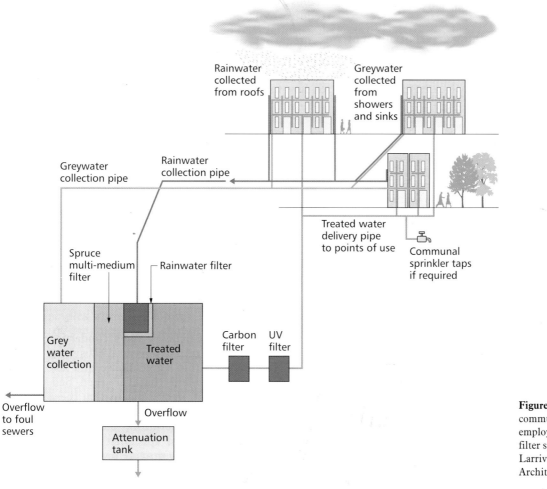

**Figure 23** Schematic of a communal grey water system employing a biological media filter system (courtesy of Kathryn Larriva at Feilden Clegg Bradley Architects)

fluorinated gas contained in the equipment: at least once a year for 3 kg or more; at least two times a year for 30 kg or more; at least four times a year for 300 kg

— operators to ensure trained and certified personnel take care of recycling, reclamation or destruction of fluorinated greenhouse gases

— all products containing fluorinated greenhouse gases need to be identified by labels (form will be set by the European Commission).

Building services engineers should advise clients that these requirements will increase the maintenance costs of equipment containing F-gas refrigerants for building operators.

For further information on the F-gas regulations refer to:

— Regulation (EC) No. 842/2006 on certain fluorinated greenhouse gases[109] (2006)

For further information on refrigerants refer to:

— CIBSE GN01: *CFCs, HCFCs and halons: professional and practical guidance on substances which deplete the ozone layer*[108] (2000).

### 5.3.2.2 Air quality management

Local authorities produce Local Air Quality Management Areas in order to monitor and control air quality in certain areas.

Nine substances are monitored: sulphur dioxide ($SO_2$), particulate patter (PM10); carbon monoxide (CO), nitrous oxides ($NO_x$), ozone ($O_3$), hydrocarbons, benzene, 1,3-butadiene and toxic organic micropollutants. Of these, some will arise from activities on site, such as vehicle use (CO) and dust (PM10) and some, such as $NO_x$, will depend on the type of equipment specified and in particular on the type of boiler.

$NO_x$ is an air pollutant that contributes to air pollution through the conversion by sunlight to ozone which is an irritant. It also contributes to more widescale problems such as acid rain.

Transport is the prime source of $NO_x$ emissions; however, other sources such as electricity production at fossil-fuelled power stations and boiler plants contribute significantly. Boiler manufacturers can provide the relevant $NO_x$ emissions data.

As a guideline, BREEAM[3] (the Building Research Establishment Environmental Assessment Method for buildings) awards most credits for boilers with $NO_x$ emissions of less than 40 mg/kW·h and none for boilers with $NO_x$ emissions of more than 100 mg/kW·h. In the case of electric heating systems, using grid electricity, the $NO_x$ emissions of power plants have to be taken into account, which are considerably higher (1200–1400 mg/kW·h)[97].

### 5.3.3 Key actions

Building services engineers should advise clients of the maintenance and operational implications associated with using F-Gas refrigerants, such as R134a and R407c.

In particular, from 4th July 2007, building services operators will have a legal obligation to monitor equipment that uses more than 3 kg of F-gas, and personnel involved in handling HFCs are likely to require nationally approved training and certification. These regulations will be reviewed in 2008 when fixed mobile air conditioning will come under increasing scrutiny.

Building services engineers should specify low $NO_x$ emission boilers and ensure that electricity generating plant on site, such as CHP is designed to limit air pollutants.

## 5.4 Health and wellbeing

The average person in the UK spends nearly 90% of their time in buildings and therefore to attain a good quality of life, internal conditions in the built environment must be comfortable. There is evidence that good quality internal environments will also improve productivity and consequently lead to financial benefits.

'Health', as defined by the World Health Organisation, is a state of complete physical, mental and social wellbeing. In the context of the built environment this can be determined by internal conditions such as air, noise, visual and thermal comfort, as well as by external environmental factors such as biodiversity and local air quality. Therefore to achieve good health and wellbeing, measures should be adopted to improve these areas.

### 5.4.1 Principles

The principles to apply to health and wellbeing are:

— discharge all statutory health and safety obligations

— apply good practice in providing for the widest practical range of accessibility needs

— avoid and reduce health risk factors

— provide comfortable internal conditions.

Refer to the CIBSE online sustainable engineering tool[2] for practical measures and sources of guidance for each of these principles (http://www.cibse.org/sustain).

These principles would be applied by the project team and the last principle, in particular, would be applied by the building services engineer.

### 5.4.2 Comfortable and healthy internal conditions

The provision of comfortable and healthy internal conditions requires the issues shown in Table 27 to be addressed.

### 5.4.3 Key actions

The building services engineers should establish the likely internal noise levels, daylight levels, internal air quality and thermal comfort conditions. Engineers should ensure that the proposals provide attractive, comfortable and appropriate internal conditions that promote health and wellbeing, as set out in the guidance below.

**Table 27** Health and wellbeing issues

| Issue | Requirement |
| --- | --- |
| Thermal comfort | Provide controls to allow independent adjustment of heating and cooling systems by occupants. |
| Internal air quality | Minimise internal air pollution. |
| | Provide efficient filters. |
| | Regular cleaning to avoid build up of dust or mould. |
| | Be aware of materials, e.g. paint or insulation that may be polluting. |
| Ventilation rates | Provide adequate fresh air rates to dilute contaminants whilst minimising the loss/gain of heat. |
| | Provide adequate crossflow of fresh air. |
| | Provide openable windows. |
| Natural lighting | Improve the quality of daylighting (and provide effective local occupant control of artificial electric lighting. |
| Glare control | Minimise problems associated with glare. |
| Internal noise | Internal noise is a recognised health hazard by the World Health Organisation. Refer to BS 8233[110] and CIBSE Guide B, chapter 5[111]. |
| Vibration | Assess vibration against criteria in BS 6472[112] or CIBSE Guide B, chapter 5[111]. |
| Humidification (Legionellosis) | Avoid risk of illness related to microbial contamination of humidification systems. |
| | Ensure cooling towers/evaporative condensers are properly designed and maintained. |
| | Ensure that hot and cold water systems are properly designed and maintained. |

For further information and guidance, refer to:

— Building Research Establishment Environmental Assessment Method (BREEAM): *Offices*[97] (2005) (http://www.breeam.org/)

— HSE: The Health and Safety at Work Act 1974[113]. See also HSE Local Authority Circular LAC 23/17: *Enforcing authority*[114] (2001) (http://www.hse.gov.uk/lau/lacs/23-17.htm). Information specifically for small businesses can be found at the Health and Safety Executive website (http://www.hse.gov.uk/aboutus/hse/policy/strategy.htm).

— HSE Local Authority Circular LAC 75/1: *Sick building syndrome*[115] (2000) (http://www.hse.gov.uk/lau/lacs/75-1.htm)

— BS 8233: *Sound insulation and noise reduction for buildings. Code of practice*[110] (1999)

— CIBSE LG10: *Daylighting and window design*[116] (1999).

## 5.5 Waste management and recycling

It is essential that suitable waste management facilities be provided for a building. Such facilities should provide adequate storage for recyclable waste and residual waste. Where appropriate, sufficient space should be provided to allow for the on-site treatment of commercial and/or household waste, equipment and containers should be accommodated to enable efficient management of waste[117].

For strategic waste management guidance see section 3.9 above.

### 5.5.1 Principles

> The principles to apply to waste management and recycling are:
>
> — reduce waste
>
> — reuse materials and equipment (and facilitate future reuse)
>
> — recycle waste (and facilitate recycling)
>
> — compost biodegradable waste
>
> — recover energy from waste (and facilitate energy recovery from waste).
>
> Refer to the CIBSE online sustainable engineering tool[2] for practical measures and sources of guidance for each of these principles (http://www.cibse.org/sustain).

These principles would be applied by the project team. Examples of measures that should be applied by the building services engineer are included below.

### 5.5.2 Design of waste recycling areas

Considerations for the design of waste recycling areas include the following:

— ease of access for site users

— ease of access for waste collectors and collection vehicles

— provision of sufficient space

— protection against rodents scavenging

— ease of maintenance and cleaning

— ventilation of storage area

— provision of adequate lighting

— provision of sound insulation

— noise (particularly in location of glass handling/collection areas)

— safety from fire risk and smoke

— aesthetic of storage area.

The waste management strategy (see section 3.9) will have:

— predicted the likely volumes and types of waste arising from the development

— considered the design and servicing of the recyclable waste storage areas

— considered the equipment required to process the waste (e.g. compactors, in-vessel composters etc.).

### 5.5.3 Servicing considerations

Building services engineers need to consider the following issues when designing services for waste management facilities:

— power provision for compactors, bailers, shredders and crushers

— water supply for waste management areas for cleaning

— drainage system for waste water.

Further information is provided in CIBSE Guide G[(65)].

### 5.5.4 Key actions

The buildings services engineers should ensure that:

— the storage space for the efficient management of waste and recyclable material is incorporated into the layout

— liaison takes place between planning authorities and architects, as well as collection authorities

— the storage space for waste and recycling is serviced and managed in accordance with CIBSE and other guidance.

Further guidance can be found in:

— BS 5906: *Waste management in buildings. Code of practice*[(117)] (2005)

— CIBSE Guide G: *Public health engineering*[(65)] (2004)

— BS PAS 100: *Specification for composted materials*[(118)] (2002)

## 5.6 Selection of materials and equipment

Selection of sustainable materials and equipment involves evaluating each decision against a range of related criteria relating to their environmental performance. These criteria relate to the extraction, sourcing, manufacture, maintenance and disposal of materials in relation to their performance and use. The key criteria are summarised in the principles set out below.

### 5.6.1 Principles

> The principles to apply relating to selection of sustainable materials are:
>
> — select materials and equipment from sustainable sources
>
> — select materials and equipment with the lowest in-use environmental impacts
>
> — select materials and equipment with the lowest embodied environmental impacts
>
> — select materials and equipment with high recycled content.
>
> Refer to the CIBSE online sustainable engineering tool[(2)] for practical measures and sources of guidance for each of these principles (http://www.cibse.org/sustain).

These principles would be applied by the project team. The building services engineers should work with the structural engineer and architect to ensure that lifecycle impacts are considered when selecting materials and equipment.

Guidance on early design decisions relating to lifecycle impacts of materials and equipment is set out in section 3.10. This guidance includes information on the use of recycled materials from demolition and the choice of construction methods.

When specifying and procuring materials and equipment, preference should be given to those that are more sustainable over their lifetime. This involves comparing a range of environmental, social and economic impacts arising throughout the product lifecycle (in production, in use and at end of life) and making an overall judgement as to which is preferable. Environmental, social and economic impacts generally have to be considered separately as there is no way of comparing these different types of impact.

The main sustainability issues that can be judged for materials and equipment relate to resource efficiency (e.g. how much energy and water is used, and how much waste is generated) and associated emissions throughout their lifecycles, i.e. from the extraction of raw materials, through manufacturing, to use and eventual management as waste (hopefully including reuse, recycling, etc.).

Assessing lifecycle impacts is highly complex and requires a large data gathering exercise. Therefore, building services engineers will be reliant on independent certification as set out below.

### 5.6.2 Select materials and equipment from sustainable sources

Preference should be given to materials and equipment from sustainable sources. This includes materials such as recycled newspaper insulation and most commonly timber products.

The world's forests are vital natural resources which are in danger due to increasing population, clearance for cash crops and subsistence farming, and illegal and unsustainable logging.

There are a number of independent schemes that certify that timber and forestry products have originated from well-managed forests.

The UK government's 'Centre Point for Expertise on Timber' (CPET) has approved five schemes that, at the time of writing, satisfy the requirements for either sustainable and/or legal timber. These schemes are:

— Programme for the Endorsement of Forest Certification (PEFC)

— Forest Stewardship Council (FSC)

— Canadian Standards Association (CSA)

— Malaysian Timber Certification Council (MTCC)

— Sustainable Forestry Initiative (SFI).

It is crucial to have a full 'chain of custody' to certify that there is a record of the path of the timber from forests to consumers. Wood must be tracked from the forest site to the finished product. BREEAM[97] considers the FSC and CSA schemes to have the most rigorous approach to responsible sourcing.

It is essential to ensure that all timber products are from recycled sources or are certified by one of the five certification schemes listed above.

For more information see:

— Department for Environment, Food and Rural Affairs (DEFRA): Central Point of Expertise for Timber Procurement (http://www.proforest.net/cpet).

### 5.6.3 Select products with the lowest in-use environmental impacts

The selection of materials with low operational impacts are generally limited to assessments of their energy and water use. Examples of schemes that rate products include:

— Department for Environment, Food and Rural Affairs (DEFRA): The *Energy Technology List* and *Water Technology List* provide comprehensive lists of products that are eligible for Enhanced Capital Allowances[119] (http://www.eca.gov.uk)

— Department for Environment, Food and Rural Affairs (DEFRA): *Energy Labels: Helping you make the right choice*[120] (2004). EU energy labels rate the energy performance of domestic products such as fridges and washing machines.

Materials also have impacts during their use and the following should be avoided where possible:

— Many common refrigerants contain HFCs, which contribute to climate change (see section 5.3.2).

— Certain paints can produce emissions, primarily formaldehyde and VOCs, which can affect indoor air quality.

A BREEAM[97] assessment will require that if hazardous materials are known to be present, then a suitable method of recording their presence in a Health and Safety file is required. This applies to:

— asbestos

— lead pipework

— lead based paints

— urea formaldehyde in foam insulation

— controlled substances such as refrigerants (see section 5.3.2)

— HCFC/HFC blown foams, such as insulants.

### 5.6.4 Select materials and equipment with lowest embodied environmental impacts

The *Green Guide to Specification*[5] provides a simplified method of comparing building elements according their overall environmental impact, based on a life cycle assessment approach. This can be used to select building components with a reduced life cycle impact.

Environmental product declarations are being used by some manufacturers to demonstrate the life cycle impacts of their products.

BS ISO 14025[121] intends to define a general, widely acceptable approach to life cycle assessment of products based on environmental product declarations. A detailed methodology for this approach is unlikely to be available until 2008.

Some manufacturers have developed environmental product declarations using systems such as the BRE environmental profiling method that uses 'ecopoints' to compare different materials and building components. The environmental rating is based on the same A, B and C rating scale as the *Green Guide to Specification*[5] (see above). Those with A-ratings will have lower overall environmental impact than those with B-ratings and both will have lower environmental impact than those with C-ratings.

Environmental product declarations can be used by the project team to determine preferable suppliers or manufacturers.

### 5.6.5 Key actions

The project team should evaluate materials and components against environmental criteria, specifically:

— select materials based on the overall environmental impacts by using a life cycle assessment (LCA) approach, such as the *Green Guide to Specification*[5]

— select suppliers or manufacturers who can provide environmental product declarations

— ensure that all timber and timber products are from recycled sources or are certified by one of the five certification schemes approved by the Central Point of Expertise for Timber Procurement

— avoid use of environmentally-hazardous materials such as insulants with global warming gases (HFCs)

— provide appropriate thermal mass whilst considering the environmental impact of the materials.

For more information and guidance, refer to:

— Anderson J and Shiers D: *Green Guide to Specification*[5] (2002)

— ECD Energy and Environment Ltd: *Greening NES: a guide to sustainable engineering specification*[69] (2001) (http://www.hostedfabermaunsell.com/greennes/greennes.pdf).

— Woolley T et al: *Green Building Handbook*[122] (2001).

## 5.7 Local environment and community

The impact of projects on the local environment and community are related to the construction and operation of buildings.

The construction site impacts relating to dust, noise and communication with the local community are addressed in section 6.

### 5.7.1 Principles

> The principles to apply to the social impacts relating to developments are:
>
> — engage with the local community throughout the building lifecycle
>
> — maintain and enhance environmental quality
>
> — avoid nuisance pollution levels (including noise)
>
> — avoid causing other nuisances to neighbourhood building users
>
> Refer to the CIBSE online sustainable engineering tool[2] for practical measures and sources of guidance for each of these principles (http://www.cibse.org/sustain).

These principles would be applied by the project team.

Issues relating to maintaining and enhancing environmental quality are addressed in section 3.11.3

Avoiding pollution and nuisance during the operation of the building are important considerations.

Excessive noise from installed plant can be a permanent source of noise nuisance to neighbours when buildings are in use. Building services engineers should give careful consideration to avoid selecting plant that may create additional noise over the existing background level, particularly at night. Alternatively, acoustic screens or an enclosure can be specified for plant elements in open air, e.g. on roof tops.

## 5.8 Alternative arrangements for providing sustainable technologies

There is an opportunity to consider alternative arrangements for providing and maintaining infrastructure and to work with utility companies to establish more sustainable methods of providing the required services.

In particular, energy and waste water services infrastructure can be funded, delivered, operated and maintained via independent companies.

### 5.8.1 Energy service companies

An infrastructure company (InfraCo) or energy services company (ESCo) can provide funding, delivery and operation of energy services, particularly for large sites. This helps to avoid large capital costs of plant and equipment. Typically, these bodies would be responsible for delivering a secure, competitively-priced supply to residents and businesses, coordinating and maintaining the infrastructure and collecting revenues to ensure an ongoing operation. This body could also be set up to deliver broader benefits for the community, and various bodies, potentially including a community trust that would have a stake in its governance.

### 5.8.2 Multi-utility provision

There are significant environmental, economic and operational advantages to be gained by integrating the energy strategy and systems with other utilities.

These principally stem from the utilisation of outputs of one system as inputs of another; for example, treated foul water as a source of non-potable water and solid waste as a potential energy source. In addition, it allows holistic consideration of the impacts of utilities, for example the energy demand of water and waste processing facilities. It also facilitates maximisation of the potential amenity benefits which could be created by an integrated system, such as the use of drainage water to enhance public space and to recharge local rivers.

Thus this integrated approach promotes the most effective use of resources, allowing energy efficiency, minimisation of water usage, and full use of waste as a resource, while promoting broader social and economic benefits. An integrated operation may also facilitate cost savings by avoiding waste disposal costs etc.

Examples of sustainable water, wastewater, energy and waste management solutions include:

— utilising groundwater sources, rainwater harvesting and grey water recycling to meet non-potable water demands (e.g. toilet flushing and irrigation), to reduce water usage by 20–40%

— developing and maintaining black water recycling systems, to provide non-potable water for recycling purposes and significantly reduce foul water discharge to sewers; solid waste may be used as a feed stock in anaerobic digestion and the production of biogas

— developing and maintaining sustainable urban drainage systems and associated habitat creation

— developing and maintaining tri-generation (i.e. combined cooling, heating and power (CCHP)) plants that may be used to supply communal cold and hot water systems as well as helping to meet renewables targets

— other renewable energy options: e.g. photovoltaic roof tiles, wind turbines, fuel cells, and biomass boilers linked to a municipal waste management strategy

— composting or digestion of green domestic waste.

A multi-utility business model allows for 'non-adoptable' assets such as grey water re-use or SUDS to be operated and maintained by multi-utility joint ventures over a long-term contract period or in perpetuity, given the appropriate long term funding.

## 6 Construction

This section considers how building services engineers can make projects more sustainable during the construction phase through their role as resident engineers.

Resident engineers have four roles during the construction phase of a project:

— where possible, ensuring that sustainability criteria are included in the selection of suppliers and sub-contractors

— ensuring that the engineering services that are procured and delivered to site meet the performance standards relating to sustainability, and that the requirements are fully addressed

— observing construction site practices and commenting on practices that could have a significant impact on the environment

— preparing handover information, in particular the building log book.

## 6.1 Procurement

Where possible, resident engineers should ensure that sustainability criteria are included in the selection of suppliers and sub-contractors and that they are made aware of the sustainability objectives for the project. Preference should be given to companies who:

— have a published environmental policy that has commitment from the top levels of management

— clearly describe the sustainable features and associated client benefits of their service offering

— have achieved recognition for sustainable behaviour (e.g. award winners); avoid those with a history of unsustainable behaviour (e.g. companies fined for breaches of environmental regulation)

— operate an environmental management system (EMS), ideally one accredited to a recognised standard such as BS EN ISO 14001[123], BS 8555[124], or the Institute of Environmental Management & Assessment's Acorn scheme[125]

— report on their sustainability performance.

It is important that all relevant tender packages be reviewed against the sustainability requirements for the project.

It is recommended that a system is set up to record and check that each key item of plant meets the specified sustainability requirements. For example, the system would highlight that chillers include refrigerant leak detection.

## 6.2 Construction site impacts

The lead contractors should prepare a comprehensive 'Environmental Aspects and Risk Assessment' for the site to identify all the construction environmental impacts and protective measures to eliminate or reduce these impacts. This would include an assessment of significant environmental aspects that considers:

— emissions to air, water and land

— management of waste

— use of raw materials and natural resources

— community issues, and

— the demolition phase.

Based on this assessment, the contractor should then prepare and implement a 'Construction Environmental Management Plan' to manage the social and environmental impacts of the construction process.

The construction process can have considerable impacts on the local but also global environment. Below are some examples of how some of the impacts can be addressed:

— Reduce carbon dioxide emissions from energy use by monitoring site electricity and fuel use and identify where energy efficiency measures could be implemented.

— Reduce carbon dioxide emissions from transport by using efficient fuel such as liquefied petroleum gas (LPG) or duel fuel vehicles.

— Minimise waste production by operating in accordance to site waste management plans (see DTI code of practice[126]).

— Minimise air, water and soil pollution by following good practice guidance (see CIRIA C651[127]).

— Reduce noise pollution by following good practice guidance (see CIRIA C651[127]).

— Follow good neighbourliness guidance by reducing impacts of construction on the local community (see BRE Report 472[128]).

The Considerate Constructors Scheme (http://considerate constructorsscheme.org.uk) is a code of considerate site practice, which can be adopted by participating construction companies and everyone involved on the construction site in order to ensure that issues concerning the environment and neighbours will be taken into account during the construction process.

The Code commits contractors in the scheme to be considerate and good neighbours, clean, respectful, safe, environmentally conscious, responsible and accountable.

## 6.3 Supporting the development of local jobs

Community benefits can arise from the employment and training opportunities presented by new developments.

Design teams should give consideration to the following:

— for large projects, establish a job centre on site, enabling local people to be recruited into jobs in both existing local businesses and new employment opportunities created by the construction and subsequent occupation of a new development

— obtain commitment from the developer and contractor that procedures to open job opportunities for local people will be implemented

— team-up with local training centres to provide apprenticeship training opportunities on site, and waged construction training.

For further information refer to:

— Department of Trade and Industry (DTI): Respect for People programme (http://www.dti.gov.uk/ sectors/construction/peopleissues/respect/page 10919.html)

—    Department for Work and Pensions (DWP): New Deal programme (http://www.jobcentreplus.gov.uk/JCP/Customers/New_Deal/index.html)

—    ConstructionSkills: Sector Skills Agreement (http://www.constructionskills.net)

## 6.4      Building log books and occupant guides

Building services engineers should prepare a building log book, as required by Building Regulations Approved Document L2[17]. This log book should be a simple 'users handbook' to help operate the building and should include performance monitoring and a system to record changes to the building (and to the log book itself)[129].

Prior to handover, the design team should train the facilities manager (FM) to use the building log book.

The building services engineer should also prepare an occupants user guide (or tenant handbook) that provides advice for the building users on lighting controls, blinds etc., as well as information on public transport links.

## 6.5      Key actions

The resident engineer would undertake the following:

—    ensure that suppliers and sub-contractors are made aware of the sustainability objectives for a project, and where possible, ensure that sustainability criteria are included in the selection of companies

—    set up a system, in collaboration with the contractor, to check and record that the sustainability requirements for key items of plant are met

—    ensure that the contractor sets up and implements site waste management plans and a construction environmental management plan

—    observe construction site practice and raise concerns about any potential environmental damage (e.g. fuel spills, contamination of water courses etc.)

—    prepare a building log book.

Further information can be found in:

—    Office of Government Commerce (OGC): *Achieving sustainability in construction procurement: Sustainability Action Plan*[130] (2000)

—    CIRIA C651: *Environmental good practice on site*[127] (2005)

—    Department of Trade and Industry (DTI): *Site waste management plans. Guidance for construction contractors and clients. Voluntary Code of Practice*[126] (2004)

—    BRE Report 472: *Working with the community — a good practice guide for the construction industry*[128]

—    CIBSE TM31: *Building log book toolkit*[129] (2006).

# 7         Buildings in use

This section discusses how the sustainability outcomes of buildings in use can be improved, particularly in terms of their environmental performance.

Design and quality of construction determines the broad range of possible sustainability outcomes for a building, but the actual outcomes depend ultimately on how a building is used, i.e. how it is managed by its owners, how its facilities are operated, and how occupants, visitors etc. then interact with those facilities.

Mechanisms and opportunities for services engineers to influence operational sustainability typically include:

—    managing commissioning and periodically re-commissioning building services systems

—    monitoring and post-occupancy evaluation, particularly of innovative systems

—    facilities engineering and operational management

—    energy management and energy audits

—    design and management of small works to building services

—    design and management of major upgrades to building services systems

—    *ad hoc* inspections and surveys.

## 7.1      Achieving sustainability in operation

Once buildings are in use, the main sustainability issues tend to be related to occupant wellbeing and resource use, i.e.:

—    internal environmental quality

—    thermal comfort

—    acoustic environment

—    internal air quality

—    energy use and carbon emissions

—    water use

—    waste management.

Improving sustainability outcomes in existing buildings and maintaining good performance depends on:

—    everyday behaviour and decisions by occupants and facilities operators

—    medium term decision-making on maintenance strategy and investment in sustainability improvements

—    longer term decisions on upgrading major items of building fabric and plant.

The pressure to keep buildings operational may conflict with implementing the most sustainable solutions or undertaking processes in a more sustainable manner.

## 7.2 Commissioning and re-commissioning

The proper commissioning of building services is crucial to ensure the correct operation of the system and its associated building services plant[131].

Commissioning affects both the effectiveness and efficiency of building services and hence the comfort of occupants, and the environmental and financial costs of maintaining it. Inefficient services will use more energy than necessary to maintain comfortable conditions resulting in greater emissions of $CO_2$ and other pollutants, and higher fuel bills.

Building Regulations approved Document L[17] includes requirements relating to commissioning. CIBSE Commissioning Code M[131] and other documents provide extensive guidance on good practice and on meeting these requirements.

The need for re-commissioning of services arises where significant changes are made to systems or to the physical configuration of a building, either of which can reduce the systems' efficiency or effectiveness. An example of a physical change to a building that might require re-commissioning of building services is a move from open plan to cellular office space, or vice versa. Services should also be periodically re-commissioned to ensure that they are operating as intended and to reset what may have been intended as short term changes to setpoints and system settings.

For further information, refer to:

— CIBSE Commissioning Code M: *Commissioning management*[131]

— BSRIA AG05/02: *Commissioning management: how to achieve a fully functioning building*[132] (2002)

## 7.3 Post occupancy evaluation

Post occupancy evaluation provides invaluable feedback for the design, refurbishment, refit and the operation of buildings.

The evaluation uses occupant surveys and monitoring data to determine whether the building performs as intended and meets the user's needs. The results can be used to identify problems that need to be addressed in the building and to help to inform the approach to future projects.

There is increasing pressure to use novel building systems to reduce carbon emissions and to cope with the impacts of climate change. Where such systems are installed, budgets should be agreed for undertaking post occupancy evaluation and monitoring. This should aim to collate and analyse occupant feedback on the performance of the systems on meeting their needs. Quantitative data should also be collected on issues such as energy generation and use, internal temperatures, efficiency of plant in operation etc.

## 7.4 Facilities engineering, maintenance and operation

As well as the activities described in the sections below, facilities engineering and operational management may involve:

— specifying planned preventative maintenance

— specifying and procuring a variety of maintenance contracts for building services systems.

The process of supporting a building owner or occupier to specify, tender, and then manage and evaluate contracts for the operation and maintenance of facilities provides many opportunities to address sustainability issues. Ideally sustainability should be built into the requirements — often 'service level agreements' — for service providers based on clear objectives and then the performance monitored and evaluated, as follows:

— Establish sustainability objectives based on the client's corporate sustainability policy.

— Include sustainability objectives and targets in the brief for contract services.

— Identify specific sustainable good practice requirements where possible and include in service level agreements.

— Make the schedule of sustainability objectives, targets and service requirements part of the agreed contract.

— Require the contractor to report regularly on their performance against sustainability issues in the building.

— Include sustainability in the evaluation of contractor performance.

The maintenance strategy influences design decisions and therefore needs to be established before the start of detailed design. When the property and its services become fully operational, the maintenance strategy must be implemented and any revisions carefully assessed to determine the impact of any such changes on original design decisions. Guidance on developing a maintenance strategy is set out in CIBSE's *Guide to ownership, operation and maintenance of building services*[133].

For further information see:

— Occupying Buildings Sustainably (OBS) website: *Managing and occupying buildings sustainably* (http://www.mobs.org.uk)

— CIBSE: *Guide to ownership, operation and maintenance of building services*[133].

## 7.5 Energy and water management

Current sustainability drivers and utilities costs can be expected to provide a growing incentive for improving energy and water management in buildings. Engineers can contribute indirectly through provision of effective log books, and may also be directly involved in energy and water management activities as follows:

— *Audits*: a specific exercise to establish the quantity and end use split of energy/water use, identify problems currently resulting in use higher than benchmarks and draw up a prioritised list of energy saving opportunities, costs and business case.

— *Monitoring and targeting*: the basis of a monitoring and targeting (M&T) system is the collection of meter readings and the interpretation of data obtained. This information can be processed and returned to sites in the form of cost and consumption management and energy accounting reports. Interpretation of the data can be used for further, and more accurate, monitoring.

— *Building log books*: energy performance can be recorded and compared with appropriate benchmarks and the designer's estimates of what the building should consume. Regular main and subsidiary meter readings can be recorded on the meter reading pro-forma set up by the log book author. Overall performance and end-use performance can then be observed over time and compared to good practice benchmarks and design estimates. Log books should be prepared prior to handover of the building (see section 6.4.).

— *Benchmarking*: learning by comparison with peers, in this case comparing the performance of a subject building with other similar buildings. Comparison can be either specific or through aggregated data, i.e. using 'benchmarks' that characterise the performance of a comparable set of buildings. The Carbon Trust (http://www.carbontrust.co.uk) provides energy and carbon emission benchmarks for a variety of existing building types. *Ad hoc* benchmarking clubs can enable comparison against specific 'peer' buildings or organisations. There are also examples of sectoral benchmarking (schools, retail, offices, hospitality) organised by third parties.

— *Carbon management*: this is a process to manage and reduce carbon emissions by engaging with relevant stakeholders, developing strategy and identifying carbon reduction opportunities. More information can be found on the Carbon Trust website (http://www.carbontrust.co.uk).

For further information see:

— CIBSE Guide F: *Energy efficiency in buildings*[16] (2004)

— CIBSE TM31: *Building log book toolkit*[129] (2006)

— The Carbon Trust: Energy Consumption Guides (various titles) (http://www.carbontrust.co.uk).

## 7.6      Small works

The management of occupied buildings frequently incorporates churn and refurbishment projects, as well as day-to-day facilities management. Although often straightforward in engineering terms, these small projects can have major implications in terms of logistics and disruption and they are usually fast track.

The best way to ensure that sustainability measures are implemented in such fast track small projects is to integrate good practice requirements into standard spec-

ifications and working practices. Changes may need to be flagged and reinforced with additional guidance and training to help them become 'embedded', particularly if they replace long standing practices, or have implications in terms of additional project effort and/or cost.

The CIBSE online sustainable engineering tool[2] (http://www.cibse.org/sustain) lists many of the good practice measures that should be considered for integration into standard working documentation.

## 7.7      Re-engineering systems

Replacing or retrofitting large parts of systems or major components represents a major opportunity to address sustainability and particularly resource use issues (energy, $CO_2$ emissions and water). A boiler, chiller or other refrigeration plant, equipment for hot water generation, and certainly a whole air conditioning system are likely to be major end users.

## 7.8      Inspections and surveys

In existing building these typically include:

— 'due diligence' surveys

— condition surveys.

The aims of such surveys are generally:

— to identify legal, financial and reputational risks

— to establish status of fabric, plant and equipment

— to identify works or replacements required, establish when they should take place, and estimate the costs and implications of these works.

Such surveys offer an ideal opportunity to establish the status of a building in relation to a wide range of sustainability issues, not just energy and $CO_2$ emissions. Established assessment methods such as BREEAM[3] are useful to establish the scope of issues to investigate and the criteria against which status can be established, even if formal assessments are not appropriate.

## 7.9      Key actions

The following actions can be taken by the building services engineer involved in work associated with operating buildings:

— Ensure that the system is operating according to design intent, which may involve periodic recommissioning.

— Recommend that sustainability is addressed when the building owner or occupier specifies tenders and evaluates contracts for the operation and maintenance of facilities.

— Ensure that refurbishment or refit projects implement the relevant sustainability principles, as set out in this Guide.

— Undertake energy and water management activities including audits and benchmarking to identify potential for further savings.

— Recommend that projects to re-engineer systems consider potential re-use of materials or systems.

— Ensure that audits and condition surveys include assessment against key sustainability drivers and targets, as identified in this Guide.

Refer to the CIBSE online sustainable engineering tool[2] (http://www.cibse.org/sustain) to identify detailed measures for improving performance.

# 8 End of life

This section sets out the sustainability issues relating to the end of the building's life.

The first preference should be for reuse or refurbishment of the building. However, if the building has reached the end of its life, then the key sustainability issue is to identify the materials and components in the building that can be reclaimed, recycled or reused.

The construction and building industries consume huge quantities of materials. The environmental impact of the extraction, gathering and production of these materials is large and growing. Moreover, when buildings are constructed large quantities of materials are wasted and most of these are sent to landfill.

The *Demolition Protocol*[72] was developed by a team led by Institution of Civil Engineers (ICE), London Remade and EnviroCentre Ltd.

The protocol describes practical methodologies for the assessment and recovery of demolition material and the potential for specifying recovered (recycled and reclaimed) material in the new build (see section 3.10.3.1).

The protocol shows how a building demolition audit can be used to generate a demolition recovery index (DRI). The DRI allows project teams to identify the potential for cost-effectively recovering material from demolition.

The maximum benefit from material will be obtained if a building is taken apart methodically, with the processes geared to create waste streams of the following:

— *concrete*: producing recycled concrete aggregate (RCA)

— *masonry*: e.g. clay brick, producing recycled aggregate (RA)

— *steel*: has a high reclaim value

— *non-ferrous metals*: e.g. copper, aluminium etc., have high reclaim value

— *wood*: structural timber has high reclaim value

— *plastics*: e.g. PVC, are potential reclaimable materials of the future

— *glass*: has a high recycling value

— *mixed waste*: difficult items such as plasterboard, which reduce the value of other waste streams.

A demolition audit allows the potential of a building to be properly assessed through the creation of a bill of quantities. This identifies the material/component in terms of the above categories, with tonnages and percentages of recycled/reuse opportunities detailed. The production of this bill of quantities will allow the project team to identify the full potential of the demolition material, by identifying where the material can be reused or re-manufactured and recycled, and the quantities available.

## 8.1 Key actions

An audit should be undertaken prior to demolition commencing to identify the potential for cost effective recovery of material from demolition.

The *Demolition Protocol*[72] and associated guidance can be found at:

— www.ice.org.uk and www.aggregain.org.uk/demolition/the_ice_demolition_protocol/index.html.

# 9 Summary

Table 28 (see pages 60 and 61) shows the key actions to take on projects. It mainly applies to major new and refurbishment projects, but the principles apply to all types of projects.

**Table 28** Summary of key actions

| Key stage | Action | Section number |
| --- | --- | --- |
| Pre-inception | Identify all drivers for sustainability and ensure that appointment allows for project team to respond to these drivers. | 2.1 and 2.4 |
| | Identify risks associated with project that relate to sustainability (e.g. flood risk assessments, damage to ecological habitat, transport impacts etc.). | 2.1 and 2.2 |
| | Determine potential impact of sustainability targets (e.g. a target for a 'zero carbon development' is likely to have implications on whole project team). | 2.2 |
| | Include scope and fees for early-stage predictions of energy and water use in scope of work (early-stage energy/carbon assessments are becoming essential). | 2.4 |
| | Determine whether an environmental impact assessment (EIA) is required. | 2.4 and 4.5 |
| Strategic brief | Provide a response to the strategic brief by considering drivers for sustainability and raising issues early in the project. | 2.1 |
| | Identify any requirements in the brief that could conflict with sustainability objectives (e.g. design targets for low internal temperatures in summer). | 2.2 |
| | Identify requirements for input from specialist consultants (e.g. ecologists, acousticians etc.) | 2.4 |
| | Identify site opportunities and constraints that relate to sustainability (e.g. likely ground conditions for ground source heat pumps). | 3 |
| Project brief | Propose sustainability objectives and targets, in particular carbon and water targets in response to drivers for sustainability. | 2.2 |
| | Determine whether assessment methodologies are required (e.g. BREEAM, NEAT) and ensure that project contributes towards all relevant targets. | |
| | Ensure that design responsibilities are allocated for all critical sustainability targets, especially those relating to carbon and water use. | |
| Strategy | Undertake an initial site analysis against sustainability targets, including determining infrastructure capacity, establishing ground conditions etc. | 3 |
| | Provide rules of thumb and design guidance for project team on key issues (e.g. number of wind turbines required to meet predicted loads, or likely spaces for an energy centre). | 3 |
| | Develop an energy and carbon emissions strategy by following the principles set out in CIBSE Guide L: *Sustainability*. | 3.1 |
| | Develop a water management strategy by following the principles set out in CIBSE Guide L: *Sustainability*. | 3.2 |
| | Develop a strategy for adapting to the effects of climate change, by following the principles set out in CIBSE Guide L: *Sustainability*. | 3.3 |
| | Recommend that the project team establishes the flood risk of the site and consults with local authority to determine whether a strategic flood risk assessment has been undertaken. | 3.4 |
| | Incorporate flood resistant principles into design of building services and work with the design team to raise awareness of flood risk and flood resistance. | |
| | Recommend that project teams give consideration to the incorporation of sustainable drainage systems and the potential to integrate with rainwater collection. | 3.5 |
| | The project team should liaise with transport planners, in order to identify the scope of transportation work required by the local authority. | 3.6 |
| | Recommend that a suitably qualified ecologist be involved to undertake an ecological appraisal of the site. | 3.7 |
| | Inform project team of shading benefits of vegetation integrated into the building design and landscape (e.g. green roofs or walls). | |
| | Incorporate access and inclusion measures identified in the accessibility audit. | 3.8 |
| | Recommend that a waste management strategy be prepared for the operation of the building. | 3.9 |
| | Consider potential for energy from waste systems. | |
| | Establish the need for and feasibility of waste management facilities such as compactors, serviced storage spaces etc. | |
| | Recommend that the life cycle impacts of materials and equipment are considered by the project team and that these are considered during the selection of construction methods in terms of ventilation strategies, appropriate thermal mass etc. | 3.10 |
| | Make the project team aware of the principles of designing for deconstruction and consider the whole life of services components for recycling or reuse at the end of their life. | |
| | Recommend that there is active engagement and consultation with the local community. | 3.11 |
| | Highlight the need for consultation with the local police Architectural Liaison Officers on safety and security. | |

**Table 9.1** Summary of key actions — *continued*

| Key stage | Action | Section number |
|---|---|---|
| Supporting the planning application | Determine planning strategy and establish the information that is required for the submission. In particular, determine whether an energy strategy report (ESR) and sustainability statement (SS) are required for application. | 4 |
| | Contribute towards environmental impact assessment (EIA) (if required), particularly in relation to air quality, noise, microclimate issues, etc. | |
| Design | Identify the options for reducing demand, supplying efficiently and for providing low or zero carbon technologies. | 5.1 |
| | Propose feasible technologies and techniques to meet carbon emissions targets. | |
| | Identify the options for reducing water demand, supplying water efficiently and for use of rainwater or treatment and reuse of water. | 5.2 |
| | Propose feasible technologies and techniques to meet water use targets. | |
| | Advise clients on the maintenance and operational implications associated with using F-Gas refrigerants, such as R134a and R407c. | 5.3 |
| | Ensure that the proposals provide comfortable and appropriate internal conditions that promote health and wellbeing, as set out in the relevant guidance. | 5.4 |
| | Ensure that storage space for efficient management of waste and recyclable material during operation is incorporated into the layout and that this space is correctly serviced and managed. | 5.5 |
| | Select and source materials based on the overall environmental impacts and suppliers' declarations. | 5.6 |
| | Avoid use of environmentally-hazardous materials such as insulants with global warming gases (HFCs). | |
| | Avoid selecting or locating plant that may create additional noise over the existing background level. | 5.7 |
| | Consider alternative arrangements for providing and maintaining infrastructure and delivering services, such as ESCos and multi-utility joint ventures. | 5.8 |
| | Incorporate all technologies and techniques, as identified in the earlier design stages and refer to the CIBSE online sustainable engineering tool[2] to identify detailed measures. | Online tool |
| Construction | Recommend that contractor selection takes account of environmental credentials. | 6.1 |
| | All relevant tender packages should be reviewed against the sustainability requirements for the project. | |
| | Recommend that sub-contractor and supplier selection takes account of environmental credentials. | |
| | Recommend a periodic review of sustainability performance against objectives and targets. | |
| | Ensure that the engineering services that are procured and delivered to site meet the performance standards relating to sustainability, and that the requirements are fully addressed. | |
| | Observe construction site practices and comment on practices that could have a significant impact on the environment. | 6.2 |
| Commissioning | Ensure that systems building commissioning/re-commissioning results accord with sustainability targets and that the contractor is notified of any issues with performance. | 7.2 |
| Building handover | Provide building log book and occupant user guide for projects and ensure that there is a clear explanation of design targets and assumptions to allow comparison with actual, operational energy use. | 6.4 |
| Operation | Ensure that the system is operating according to design intent, which may involve periodic recommissioning and post-occupancy evaluation. | 7 |
| | Recommend that sustainability be addressed when the building owner or occupier specifies tenders and evaluates contracts for the operation and maintenance of facilities. | |
| | Ensure that refurbishment or refit projects implement the relevant sustainability principles, as set out in this document. | |
| | Undertake energy and water management activities including audits and benchmarking to identify potential for further savings. | |
| | Recommend that projects to re-engineer systems consider potential re-use of materials or systems. | |
| | Ensure that audits and condition surveys include assessment against key sustainability drivers and targets, as identified in this document. | |
| | Refer to the CIBSE online sustainable engineering tool[2] to identify detailed measures for improving performance. | |
| Deconstruction | An audit should be undertaken prior to demolition commencing to identify the potential for cost-effective recovery of material from demolition. | 8 |

79    *Draft Regional Spatial Strategy* (Taunton: South West Regional Assembly) (available from http://www.southwest-ra.gov.uk/ nqcontent.cfm?a_id=836) (accessed April 2007)

80    *Planning Permission — Learn how to Apply* (webpage) (London: Communities and Local Government) (available from http:// www.planningportal.gov.uk/england/genpub/en/1010677919308. html) (accessed April 2007)

81    *Consultation — Planning Policy Statement: Planning and Climate Change — Supplement to Planning Policy Statement 1* (London: Communities and Local Government) (2006) (available from http://www.communities.gov.uk/index.asp?id=1505140) (accessed April 2007)

82    Council Directive 85/337/EEC of 27 June 1985 on the assessment of the effects of certain public and private projects on the environment *Official J. of the European Communities* **L175** 40–48 (5/07/1985)

83    Council Directive 97/11/EC of 3 March 1997 amending Directive 85/337/EEC on the assessment of the effects of certain public and private projects on the environment *Official J. of the European Communities* **L073** 5 (14/03/1997)

84    *Building energy and environmental modelling* CIBSE AM11 (Chartered Institution of Building Services Engineers) (1998)

85    *Testing buildings for air leakage* CIBSE TM23 (London: Chartered Institution of Building Services Engineers) (2000)

86    *Small scale combined heat and power for buildings* CIBSE AM12 (London: Chartered Institution of Building Services Engineers) (1999)

87    *Introduction to large-scale CHP* Good Practice Guide GPG043 (Garston: Energy Efficiency Best Practice Programme) (1992 rev. 1999) (available from http://www.carbontrust.co.uk/ Publications/publicationdetail.htm?productid=GPG043&meta NoCache=1) (accessed April 2007)

88    *An introduction to absorbtion cooling* Good Practice Guide GPG256 (Garston: Energy Efficiency Best Practice Programme) (2001) (available from http://www.carbontrust. co.uk/Publications/publicationdetail.htm?productid=GPG256 &metaNoCache=1) (accessed April 2007)

89    *BedZED (Beddington Zero Energy Development) factsheet* (website) (London: Peabody Trust) (http://www.peabody. org.uk/bedzed) (accessed April 2007)

90    *Small wind energy systems* BWEA Briefing Sheet (London: British Wind Energy Association) (available from http://www. bwea.com/pdf/briefings/smallsystems.pdf) (accessed April 2007)

91    *The assessment and rating of noise from wind farms* ETSU-R-97 (London: Department of Trade and Industry) (1996) (available from http://www.dti.gov.uk/energy/sources/renewables/pub lications/page31267.html) (accessed April 2007)

92    *Non-domestic heating, cooling and ventilation compliance guide: Compliance with Approved Document L2A: New buildings other than dwellings and L2B: Existing buildings other than dwellings* (London: NBS/Department for Communities and Local Government) (2006) (available from http://www.communities. gov.uk/pub/148/NonDomesticHeatingVentilationandAirCondit ioningComplianceGuide_id1500148.pdf) (accessed April 2007)

93    *Reclaimed water* CIBSE KS01 (London: Chartered Institution of Building Services Engineers) (2005)

94    *Watermark: Final project report to HM Treasury* (London: Office of Government Commerce) (2003) (available from http:// www.ogcbuyingsolutions.gov.uk/energy/watermark/downloads/ watermark_project_final_report.pdf) (accessed April 2007)

95    Waggett R and Arotsky C *Key Performance Indicators for water use in hotels* CIRIA W10 (London: CIRIA) (2006) (available from http://www.ciria.org/downloads/01/w010.pdf) (accessed April 2007)

96    Waggett R and Arotsky C *Key Performance Indicators for water use in offices* CIRIA W11 (London: CIRIA) (2006) (available from http://www.ciria.org/downloads/01/w011.pdf) (accessed April 2007)

97    *BREEAM: Offices* (website) (Garston: Building Research Establishment) (2007) (http://www.breeam.org/page.jsp?id=17) (accessed April 2007)

98    Leggett D, Brown R, Brewer D, Stanfield G and Holliday E *Rainwater and grey water use in buildings. Best practice guidance* CIRIA C539 (London: CIRIA) (2001)

99    Leggett D, Brown R, Stanfield G, Brewer D and Holliday E *Rainwater and grey water use in buildings. Decision-making for water conservation* CIRIA PR080 (London: CIRIA) (2001)

100   Brown R and Palmer A *Water reclamation guidance: Design and construction of systems using grey water* BSRIA TN 6/2002 (Bracknell: BSRIA) (2002)

101   *Plumbing engineering services design guide* (Hornchurch: Institute of Plumbing and Heating Engineering) (2002)

102   Grant N, Moodie M and Weedon C *Sewage Solutions: Answering the call of Nature* 3rd edn. (Machynlleth: Centre for Alternative Technology Publications) (2005)

103   *This is how it works — the solution is given by nature itself!* (webpage) (Kungshamn, Sweden: Aquatron International) (http://www.aquatron.se/start.uk.html)

104   Grant N and Morgan C 'Ecological wastewater management; challenging assumptions and developing contextual design solutions' *Proc. CIBSE Nat. Conf., Harrogate, 4–5 October 1999: Engineering in the 21st century — the changing world* p576 (London: Chartered Institution of Building Services Engineers) (1999)

105   Griggs J, Grant N *Reed beds: design construction and maintenance* BRE Good Building Guide 42 Part 2 (Garston: Building Research Establishment) (2000)

106   Nuttall P M, Boon A G and Rowell M R *Review of the design and management of constructed wetlands* CIRIA R180 (London: CIRIA) (1998)

107   Griggs J, Grant N *Reed beds: application and specification* BRE Good Building Guide 42 Part 1 (Garston: Building Research Establishment) (2000)

108   *CFCs, HCFCs and halons: professional and practical guidance on substances that deplete the ozone layer* CIBSE GN1 (London: Chartered Institution of Building Services Engineers) (2000)

109   Regulation (EC) No 842/2006 of the European Parliament and of the Council of 17 May 2006 on certain fluorinated greenhouse gases ('The F-gas Regulation') *Official J. of the European Union* **L161/1** (14.6.2006) (Brussels: Commission for the European Communities) (2006)

110   BS 8233: 1999: *Sound insulation and noise reduction for buildings. Code of Practice* (London: British Standards Institution) (1999)

111   *Noise and vibration control for HVAC* ch. 5 in *Heating, ventilating, air conditioning and refrigeration* CIBSE Guide B (London: Chartered Institution of Building Services Engineers) (2001–2)

112   BS 6472: 1992: *Evaluation of human exposure to vibration in buildings (1 Hz to 80 Hz)* (London: British Standards Institution) (1992)

113   Health and Safety at Work, etc. Act 1974 Elizabeth II. Ch. 37 (London: Her Majesty's Stationery Office) (1974)

114   *Enforcing authority* HSE Local Authority Circular LAC 23/17 (London: Health and Safety Executive) (2001) (available from http://www.hse.gov.uk/lau/lacs/23-17.htm) (accessed April 2007)

115   *Sick building syndrome* HSE Local Authority Circular LAC 75/1 (London: Health and Safety Executive) (2000) (http://www. hse.gov.uk/lau/lacs/75-1.htm) (accessed April 2007)

116    *Daylighting and window design* CIBSE LG10 (London: Chartered Institution of Building Services Engineers) (1999)

117    BS 5906: 2005: *Waste management in buildings. Code of practice* (London: British Standards Institution) (2005)

118    BS PAS 100: 2005: *Specification for composted materials* (Banbury: The Waste & Resources Action Programme (WRAP)) (2005)

119    *Enhanced capital allowances* (website) (London: Department for Environment, Food and Rural Affairs) (www.eca.gov.uk) (accessed April 2007)

120    *Energy Labels — Helping you make the right choice* (London: Department for Environment, Food and Rural Affairs) (2005) (available from http://www.defra.gov.uk/environment/consumer prod/energylabels/energylabel.pdf) (accessed April 2007)

121    BS ISO 14025: 2006: *Environmental labels and declarations. Type III environmental declarations. Principles and procedures* (London: British Standards Institution) (2006)

122    Woolley T, Kimmins S, Harrison R and Harrison P *Green Building Handbook: A Guide to Building Products and Their Impact on the Environment* (vol 1) (London: Spon) (2001)

123    BS EN ISO 14001: 2004: *Environmental management systems. Requirements with guidance for use* (London: British Standards Institution) (2004)

124    BS 8555: 2003: *Environmental management systems. Guide to the phased implementation of an environmental management system including the use of environmental performance evaluation* (London: British Standards Institution) (2003)

125    *IEMA Acorn Scheme* (webpage) (Lincoln: Institute of Environmental Management and Assessment) (http://www.iema.net/acorn) (accessed April 2007)

126    *Site waste management plans. Guidance for Construction Contractors and Clients. Voluntary Code of Practice* (London: Department of Trade and Industry) (2004) (available from http://www.wrap.org.uk/downloads/site_waste_management_plan.ee3adb8a.pdf) (accessed April 2007)

127    *Environmental good practice on site* CIRIA C651 (London: CIRIA) (2005)

128    Hadi M, Rao S, Sargant H and Rathouse K *Working with the community — a good practice guide for the construction industry* BRE Report 472 (Garston: Building Research Establishment) (2004)

129    *Building log book toolkit* CIBSE TM31 (London: Chartered Institution of Building Services Engineers) (2006)

130    *Achieving sustainability in construction procurement — Sustainability Action Plan* (London: Office of Government Commerce) (2000) (available from http://www.ogc.gov.uk/documents/sustainability.pdf) (accessed April 2007)

131    *Commissioning management* CIBSE Commissioning Code M (London: Chartered Institution of Building Services Engineers) (2003)

132    Dicks M *Commissioning management: how to achieve a fully functioning building* BSRIA AG 5/2002 (Bracknell: Building Services Research and Information Association) (2002)

133    *Guide to ownership, operation and maintenance of building services* (London: Chartered Institution of Building Services Engineers) (2000)

# Index